INFORMAL LOGIC

The Allyn and Bacon Series

TOPICS IN CONTEMPORARY MATHEMATICS

INFORMAL LOGIC

John W. Kenelly

Associate Professor of Mathematics
Clemson University

Boston

ALLYN AND BACON, INC.

1967

Preface

The present emphasis on formal proofs in the elementary courses does not allow the student the luxury of time. Present programs call for a utilization of logic in the early material, and time is not allowed for a slow acquisition of the techniques through a sequence of courses. What is needed is a brief elementary analysis of symbolic logic with a mathematical orientation. This book was written to answer that need.

Formal Mathematical Logic is too involved a discipline to be of assistance at the elementary level, and a philosophical treatment of logic would lack the efficiency that is desired. Consequently this approach is informal and the results are constructed in conjunction with mathematical concepts.

The unique characteristic of this text is that its purpose is to use logical inferences and valid substitution within mathematical proofs. There is no attempt to put mathematical proofs into a formal stereotype style. In other words, logic is used as an "aside" analytical device; mathematics is not expressed in a logic format. The student is directed to explore the hidden deductions and implications of which mathematics is composed, and finally to enjoy the art of subtle proofs.

Even though the logical techniques developed are most important to college-level mathematics, the material presupposes only a knowledge of high school algebra and geometry. The examples and exercises are selected from elementary mathematics, and students should have little difficulty with the illustrations. A formal system for the ordered real number field is included, and basic definitions from analysis are employed. The analysis topics are introduced in regard to negations of definitions that involve quantifiers — — as an answer to the plea of instructors that students should be able to negate the definition of a continuous function. These topics may serve in two ways: as a prelude to mathematics at this level or as a re-examination of familiar material.

Preliminary editions have been used for about one-third of the course content in a three-semester-hour course in logic and set theory. Special appreciation is extended to Mr. P. C. Bowie, Mr. J. N. Nicholson, and Dr. J. L. Tilley for their cooperation in class-testing the material, and to Mrs. Ann Elliott, Mrs. Sue Marrah, and Miss Lois McAllister for typing the earlier material.

Two people have given an indirect but important contribution. In one case a heritage of ideals, and in the other continuing encouragement. To the memory of my father and to Mr. Jim Piles this book is dedicated.

John W. Kenelly

1966

TABLE OF CONTENTS

I

THE STATEMENT CALCULUS

Chapter 1

STATEMENT VARIABLES AND OPERATORS

§ 1 STATEMENT VARIABLES

A basic concept in logic is that of a statement. In a formal development, we would leave "statement" undefined, but here it will be defined by means of the concept of truth value. Truth value is then described in general terms, and formality is violated in the interest of understanding. *Truth Value* is assigned by the truth function τ (tau) to classifiable expressions, that is, τ assigns the letter T to true expressions and F to false expressions. To determine whether something is true or false is to apply the truth function and determine the truth status. Since τ is a function it can not assign both T and F to any particular group of symbols.

Definition 1:　An expression is a *statement* if and only if it has truth value.

It is sometimes difficult to determine an expression's truth value and its status as a statement. Simple declarative sentences are good examples of statements. For example: "December 7, 1941 is the date of a Sunday," and "December 7, 1941 is the date of a Wednesday," are two statements. The first has truth value T, and the second has truth value F. Vague expressions present certain problems, such as the expression "Monday is December 7th." Generally this type of sentence is given in a situation that tacitly supplies other information. If you said this sentence in a conversation during December of 1941, everyone would assume that you were talking about 1941 and then it would be a statement with truth value F. But outside of a context situation, this expression is not a statement simply because it is neither true nor false. We will assume that an expression given in a context situation always includes the information that is implied. This assumption will apply to mathematical expressions, the ones that we are primarily interested in. For example, "1 + 1 = 10" would be considered a statement with truth value F because we are assuming that the expression is made in base ten numerals.*

---

* In the binary base $1 + 1 = 10$ would have truth value T, and in the duo-decimal base its truth value is F, simply because unity plus unity is one-zero in the binary base numeral system and two in the duo-decimal system.

An *open sentence* falls into a different category. Such an expression has a variable in its structure, and its truth value can not be established until the variable is specified or restricted. "He is in New Orleans, Louisiana" is an open sentence, and it is not a statement until "he" is specified. Of course the context situation might apply here, but generally such an expression is considered an open sentence. The context situation usually applies to expressions like "Joe is in this room." Actually, it is almost as vague to say "Joe" as it is to say "he," but usually the individuals that are communicating know the particular Joe by context. If not, they would probably inquire, "Joe who?"

The collection of symbols "$x + 1 = 2$" is a mathematical open expression, and its truth value is not determined until the variable x is specified or restricted. We will classify the expressions with variables or pronouns as open sentences, and we will not consider them to be statements. Quantifiers are needed in the study of open sentences; and, except for a brief discussion in § 2, we will defer their investigation until the second half of the book.

The concept of truth value tacitly uses the term "determined," which needs some explanation. In mathematics, "determined" does not require that we know nor that it is humanly possible to find the indicated information. For example, "George Washington rode a white horse on January 1, 1776" is a statement. Here it is not clear whether the truth value is T or F, but the sentence does have truth value. It might be difficult or even impossible to discover the truth, but Washington did or did not ride a white horse on that day. Consequently, the sentence is a statement.

We will need symbols to represent statements, so we agree on the statement variables $p, q, r, \ldots$, as notation for statements. A *statement variable* is a representation of a statement. Within a discussion or formula, a particular statement variable is associated with a precise expression that is known to be a statement. Thus, results given in terms of statement variables apply to any situation in which the same statement is substituted for its associated variable. Occasionally, many symbols will be needed, and subscripts will be used; for example, p_1, q_1, p_3, q_{1235}. The notation $\tau(p) = T$ will be used to indicate that statement variable p has truth value T.*

* Formally a symbol p represents an equivalence class of statements.

EXERCISES (§1.)

1. Decide if the following are statements, statements when considered in context, open sentences, or none of the above.

(a) mathematics

(b) $1 + 3 = 4$

(c) $x - y = 3$

(d) Geronimo was born in the area that is now called New Mexico.

(e) Get up.

(f) Today is Tuesday.

(g) $1 + 3 = 10$

(h) Jim is active.

(i) He is in town.

(j) There are three integers x, y, z, where $x^{1000} + y^{1000} = z^{1000}$.

(k) In the year 700 B.C. the first day of the month of July was a Tuesday.

(l) With only the geometric instruments, straightedge and compass, it is usually impossible to trisect an angle.

(m) Boston is a state.

(n) This sentence is not true.

(o) Friday the thirteenth is on Thursday this month.

2. Find an example of an expression that is:

(a) a statement

(b) a statement when considered in context

(c) an open sentence from mathematics

(d) an open sentence from common discourse

(e) a non-statement

(f) hard for you to classify

(g) a statement whose truth value it is humanly impossible to decide.

5

3. Explain why it is not possible to assign truth value to sentences that assert possibilities or sentences that involve value terms, i.e., expressions that have relative interpretations. Decide if the following have truth value.

(a) Spinach has a pleasant taste.

(b) I know.

(c) I think that I know.

(d) I know that I know.

(e) It might be the case that Joe has the tickets.

(f) It is the case that Joe has the tickets.

(g) Joe probably has the tickets.

The combination of statement variables and the effect of operators in generating new statement forms is an area of prime importance in the statement calculus.* In mathematics, an operator is something that associates with an object a related object. In this sense, statement variable operators will join or "operate on" statement variables to give variable expressions that represent related statements. Logical connectives in effect combine elementary sentences very much like operators to yield complex sentences. That is, they operate on the elementary sentences to give complex sentences. We already have symbols for statements; so, we now proceed to a symbolization of the various operators that join or operate on the statements variables. These form two classes: the unary † operators and the binary operators.

§2 UNARY OPERATOR

A *unary operator* operates on one statement variable to generate a new expression for which the truth value depends only on the truth value of the original statement variable.

---

* The terms "sequential variables" and "sequential connectives" are also used for what we call statement variables and operators. We use "operators" since it is more natural in a mathematical sense.

† The reader might prefer the alternate term *unitary*.

We first observe the possible number of unary operators. In our study, truth value is the important aspect of a statement and its representing statement variable, so how many ways may new truth values be generated from the possible truth values of the statement variable? Observe that a general statement variable, p, may have one of two different truth values, either T or F. When a unary operator operates on p, it may generate a new truth value or it may retain the same truth value. So we have two choices with a change or a non-change taking place for each choice. From this idea of possible changes we see that the number of combinations is given by $2 \cdot 2$ or 4. One possible operator would retain the T's as T's and F's as F's; we will call this operator o_2. Another possible operator would change T's to F's and F's to T's; we will call this operator o_3. The other two possibilities will be called o_1 and o_4. The operators o_1, o_2, o_3, o_4, and their relations to the truth value of p are illustrated in the following table. For example whatever the operator o_1 is, it would generate an expression with truth value T whenever p has truth value T; it would also generate truth value T whenever p has truth value F.

p	$o_1(p)$	$o_2(p)$	$o_3(p)$	$o_4(p)$
T	T	T	F	F
F	T	F	T	F

There are four columns, and we would first suspect that we need to generate symbols for all four of the operators. However, this is not the case. Observe that operator o_2 has no effect, so we will dispense with it as needless in our discussion. Operators o_1 and o_4 generate constant truth values, so we will not establish symbols for them. The reason for disregarding the constant truth value columns will be more understandable when we study tautologies in a later section. This leaves only the operator o_3 to investigate.

A language equivalent to operator o_3 is that of negation of a sentence. This is, what operator o_3 does to a statement variable closely parallels the effect of negating a sentence. The negation of a true sentence is a false sentence and the negation of a false sentence is a true one. Likewise the operator o_3 changes a true statement variable to a variable with truth value F. For example "Boston is a city" can be negated to form "Boston is not a city" or "It is not the case that Boston is a city." We will employ the tilde symbol, $\sim$, to indicate negation operator o_3, and it should be verbalized as "not."*

The negation of a sentence is an elementary but involved concept. For simple declarative sentences, the negation is immediately apparent. Either a form of "not" is associated with the verb or a preface clause of "it is not the case" is introduced immediately before the sentence. Complications result when a quantifier is present. Quantifiers are investigated in the second half of the book, but it is important that we mention them here in regard to negation.

Consider the following example. The negation of "all swans are white" is "there exists a non-white swan." Observe that the negation is *not* "all swans are not white," and the negation is *not* "there exists a black swan." Remember that the negation must be a sentence that is (i) true when the original sentence is false and (ii) false when the original sentence is true. The reason for the particular negation is apparent with the observation that "all swans are not white" and "there exists a black swan" fail to be necessarily true when "all swans are white" is false. Of course the existence of a black swan would demonstrate that the statement "all swans are white" is false, but so would the existence of a green swan with diagonal red stripes.

We now formalize the definition of the negation operator. The important concept of a statement variable is its truth value, so we need only establish the truth value of $\sim p$ as a function of the truth value of p. The definition might be written as follows: $\tau(\sim p) = F$ if and only if $\tau(p) = T$, and $\tau(\sim p) = T$ if and only if $\tau(p) = F$. But it is more convenient to organize this in the form of a rectangular array, i.e., a truth table. A *truth table* is a rectangular array that pairs with each possible truth value of the statement variable(s) the new truth value generated by the operator.

Definition 2:

p	$\sim p$
T	F
F	T

---

* The tilde symbol should be placed above a letter, but we will employ it as a symbol that precedes expressions.

EXERCISES (§ 2.)

 1. Write out the negations of the following expressions.

(a) Clemson is in South Carolina.

(b) $1 + 2 = 3$

(c) Green is blue.

(d) It is not the case that Jack is at his home.

(e) It is false that New York is in England.

(f) p

(g) $\sim q$

(h) All men are mortal.

(i) Many men are outstanding.

(j) Each individual must pass the test.

(k) Everyone must leave the building before next Monday.

(l) $2 > 3$

(m) $3 \leq 5$

 2. The following expressions are the negations of various expressions. Find the original expressions.

(a) $\sim \sim p$

(b) $1 \leq 3$

(c) $6 > 7$

(d) Everyone is here.

(e) There exists a dishonest individual.

(f) There exists a pink room.

(g) p

 3. In everyday language the negation of an assertion is generally expressed with a form of not, associated with the verb. Write the commonly expressed negations of the following.

(a) John is a mathematics student.

9

(b) This course is easy.

(c) Honest people do not steal.

(d) Nobody's perfect.

(e) All integers are whole numbers.

(f) Do not hit the ball off the putting green.

(g) Hit mulligans only on the number one tee.

(h) Lazy students do not study.

(i) Positive real numbers are greater than zero.

§ 3 BINARY OPERATORS

A *binary operator* combines two statement variables to generate a new expression for which the truth value depends only on the truth values of the component statement variables.

In a manner similar to § 2, we need to determine the possible number of binary operators. We are combining two statement variables; so, we first have to establish their possible truth value occurrences. In this sense consider two statement variables p and q. There are two possible truth values for the statement variable p and two independent possible values for the statement variable q. Consequently there are $2 \cdot 2$ or 4 possible combinations of truth values for p and q.

Now how many ways can we generate new truth values, given the four possible combinations? There are two possible values, T or F, to generate when p and q both have truth value T. Likewise, there are two possible values to generate when $\tau(p) = T$ and $\tau(q) = F$; two choices when $\tau(p) = F$ and $\tau(q) = T$; and two when $\tau(p) = F$ and $\tau(q) = F$. These four independent dual choices give us a total of $2 \cdot 2 \cdot 2 \cdot 2$ or 16 columns for possible operators. These are indicated in the table.

p	q	pO_1q	pO_2q	pO_3q	pO_4q	pO_5q	pO_6q	pO_7q	pO_8q
T	T	T	T	T	T	F	T	T	F
T	F	T	T	T	F	T	T	F	F
F	T	T	T	F	T	T	F	F	T
F	F	T	F	T	T	T	F	T	T

p	q	pO_9q	$pO_{10}q$	$pO_{11}q$	$pO_{12}q$	$pO_{13}q$	$pO_{14}q$	$pO_{15}q$	$pO_{16}q$
T	T	T	F	F	F	F	F	T	F
T	F	F	T	T	F	F	T	F	F
F	T	T	F	T	F	T	F	F	F
F	F	F	T	F	T	F	F	F	F

The present problem is that we have an indication of sixteen different binary operators, and we want to study, generate specific symbols for, and define each of the sixteen. In particular, look at the fourth column and operator O_4. At present this represents some unspecified operator that combines a true statement variable p and a true variable q to give an expression with truth value T. Also it combines a true statement variable p and a false statement variable q to give an expression with truth value F. Likewise false p's with false q's give a true expression. In our later investigations we will see that the effect of this operator on statement variables parallels the language connective "if . . . , then. . . ." At that time we will assign it the symbol =>.

We indicate the combination that operator O_4 generates as $p\,O_4\,q$. The expression $p\,O_4\,q$ means that the two statement variables p and q are combined via the operator O_4 in the indicated order. That is in a way analogous to the use of the plus sign, +, to indicate the sum of two numbers, for example $2 + 3$.

There are six columns that do not require symbols, so we will generate a specific operator for only ten of the columns. The columns O_1 and O_{16} generate constant truth value columns, so we will not establish symbols for these operators. Again the reason for disregarding the constant truth value columns will be more understandable when we study tautologies in a later section. The operator O_6 generates a column of truth values that repeat the truth values of the statement variable p. Likewise the operator O_9 generates a set of truth values identical with the truth values of q. Thus we will not need an expression for $p\,O_6\,q$ or $p\,O_9\,q$ -- we would simply write p or q instead. The operation $p\,O_8\,q$

11

can be simply expressed as $\sim p$, and the operation $p \, O_{10} \, q$ can be simply expressed as $\sim q$. Consequently, we will not specify symbols for the first, sixth, eighth, ninth, tenth, and sixteenth columns. This leaves us ten columns to investigate.

3·A.   Conjunction

The operator O_{15} detailed in the fifteenth column, joins statement variables with the same effect that conjunction joins sentences in ordinary language. Observe that this operator gives the truth value T if and only if both statement variables are T, that is $\tau(p \, O_{15} \, q) = T$ if and only if $\tau(p) = T$ and $\tau(q) = T$. It corresponds to our use of the conjunction "and", so we will read it as "and." The operator is noted with the symbol "$\wedge$."* For example the sentence "George Washington was the first president and Abraham Lincoln was the sixteenth" is true since both of the conjoined statements are both true. If either statement were false, the complete sentence would be false.

In the English language, conjunction may be written in many ways: and, but, however. We are not interested in the literary emphasis that these variations add, only the resulting truth value. So we will class them all as conjunctions and translate them as "and."

Definition 3:	p	q	$p \wedge q$
	T	T	T
	T	F	F
	F	T	F
	F	F	F

It might surprise the reader to note that we now have enough symbols for all the truth value columns in the table of possible operators. The reason is that it is possible to derive each possible truth value column as an expression involving only statement variables and the conjunction and negation operators. This concept is explained in Chapter 2, §3. The reason that we continue in our discussion is that we want symbols for many language connectives and in the later sections we will investigate the various equivalences.

* Some authors use the ampersand, "&," to symbolize conjunction; and others use alternate symbols: the dot "." or the intersection symbol from set theory "∩." The caret or "inverted v" is a very popular one, so we will use it.

3·B.   Disjunction

The operator indicated in the second column is one way of symbolizing the language connective "or." The term "or" has different interpretations in the English language, so we must first investigate these various meanings. Consider the following examples: "Jack Jones is over six feet tall, or Jack Jones weighs over two hundred pounds." "Paul will eat dinner tonight in San Francisco, or Paul will eat dinner tonight in Bombay." "The price of this meal includes coffee or tea." Observe that the first expression is considered true if either statistic is true or if both are true. The second is considered true if either one of the dinner events happens exclusive of the other. The third statement is true only when you order just tea or coffee, not both. There are three different meanings attached to the same English connective. In the statement calculus we can not have this ambiguity, so we establish three different operators: inclusive disjunction, exclusive disjunction, and the Sheffer stroke.*

The first operator, "at least one," is inclusive (weak) disjunction. The sentence "Jack Jones is over six feet tall or Jack Jones weighs over two hundred pounds" illustrates the corresponding connective. We will employ the notation "$\vee$" for the inclusive disjunction of two statements, and we will read it as "or." It is operator O_2.

Definition 4:

p	q	$p \vee q$
T	T	T
T	F	T
F	T	T
F	F	F

The second type of disjunction, "exactly one," corresponds to the eleventh column. It is exclusive (strong) disjunction, and the sentence about Paul's dinner illustrates this. The only difference between

---

*   It is interesting to note how this ambiguity is handled in other situations. In the Latin language there are two or's: *aut* and *vel*. The *vel* is inclusive disjunction and the *aut* is exclusive disjunction. In legal papers the ambiguity is removed by the use of "and/or" to indicate the inclusive sense. In mathematics the term "or" is always interpreted in the inclusive sense. The situation might rule out the possibility of both, but the term should be read in the inclusive sense. Authors usually use "but not both" to specify the exclusive sense.

exclusive and inclusive disjunction is the truth value when both components are true. The notation is $p \underline{\vee} q$, and the symbol is read as "exclusive or." The notation is simply a "$\vee$" with a bar under it.

Definition 5:

p	q	$p \underline{\vee} q$
T	T	F
T	F	T
F	T	T
F	F	F

The symbol for the Sheffer stroke is "/" and it should read as "not both p and q."* It symbolizes the restaurant usage, "at most one," and it is operator O_5. In fact you might have observed "coffee/tea" on a menu; if so, it conformed to acceptable logic usage. The reader might note that this operator is the negation of conjunction.

Definition 6:

p	q	p / q
T	T	F
T	F	T
F	T	T
F	F	T

EXERCISES (§3·B.)

1. Symbolize the following expressions. Indicate the statements that the variables represent and discuss the "or" selection in relation to the usual meaning of the sentences.

(a) It is raining or the grass is wet.

(b) The point is in set A or set B.

(c) The set is open or closed.

(d) $3 \leq 5$

(e) Joe or Jim must be present.

(f) (from a checking account) Mr. or Mrs. John Smith.

---

* In reference to H. M. Sheffer although it was first noted by C. S. Peirce. Peirce is given credit for being the first person to formulate truth tables.

(g) (from a deed of a home in a common property state) Mr. or Mrs. John Smith.

(h) To win we need either a better score or a forfeit.

(i) Payment is made in case of an accident and/or death.

(j) Select ice cream or cake, but not both.

(k) Joe will marry Mary or Jane.

(l) Roses are red or violets are blue.

(m) You must fish or cut bait.

(n) Students or faculty may park here.

(o) Students or persons under eighteen years of age are admitted for half fare.

(p) The figure is either a rectangle or a square.

(q) A non-zero integer is either positive or negative.

(r) You must do one or the other of the two tasks.

(s) You may go with us or you may stay here.

(t) One either succeeds or fails.

(u) *Coq d'or*

2. Examine the definition of "or" in a dictionary.

3. The correct symbolization of the following will be more apparent after section 2 of Chapter 2, but attempt to express them now.

(a) (from a dinner menu) Coffee, tea, or milk.
Hint: the answer is not $(p \mathbin{/} q) \mathbin{/} r$.

(b) For a real number a, exactly one of the following holds: (i) $a > 0$, (ii) $a = 0$, or (iii) $a < 0$.
Hint: The answer is not $(p \veebar q) \veebar r$.

3·C   Implication

The next binary operator is perhaps the most important one to mathematics. It is the symbolization of statements of the form "if ———,

15

then ———," and we will denote it as $p \Rightarrow q$. There are many alternate ways of stating the expression "If p, then q." The popular ones are:

> p only if q
> q if p
> q is a necessary condition for p
> p is sufficient condition for q
> p implies q

Implication is the basic form of most mathematical theorems, and the p is referred to as the "hypothesis," "given part," or "antecedent"; q is referred to as the "conclusion," "to prove part," or "consequence." For correct implications, the principal concept is that whenever the hypothesis is true, the conclusion has to be true. That is why we refer to the hypothesis as a sufficient condition for the conclusion, and we refer to the conclusion as a necessary condition for the hypothesis. That is, when the hypothesis happens, this is sufficient information to know that the conclusion happens; and, for the hypothesis to hold, it is necessary that the conclusion hold.

Sufficient condition  Necessary condition

The use of the word "implies" introduces a slight element of confusion. For example, the "man in the street" would not agree with the following implication: "If for decimal numerals $3 - 1 = 3$, then all people have blond hair." His probable remark would be: "Look, numbers do not have anything to do with people having blond hair." In logic this interconnection need not be present, in fact, statements p and q may be involved with entirely different subjects. The only requirement for $p \Rightarrow q$ to have truth value T is that whenever p's truth value is T, then q's truth value must be T also. In decimal numerals, $3 - 1 = 3$ will never have truth value T, so the implication under discussion is true. That is, when $3 - 1$ is equal to 3 all people will indeed have blond hair. This points out that O_4 is the operator that corresponds to the mathematical use of "if p, then q."

The statements in an implication are replaced with symbols p, q, etc., and we have no way to refer to their content. In this sense it is impossible for us to define a "content" restriction on our implication operator.

Definition 7:

p	q	$p \Rightarrow q$
T	T	T
T	F	F
F	T	T
F	F	T

The reader might still be concerned with the last two rows in Definition 7. In this consideration the following "theorems" are given to add reassurance that the definition conforms to the intuitive concept of the expression "if p, then q." We agree, of course, that a proof of an implication assures us that the statement is true.

Theorem a   If $4 = 1$, then $5 = 5$.

Proof: $4 = 1$ Hypothesis
$1 = 4$ Symmetry of equality
∴. $5 = 5$ Addition is well defined (equals added to equals)

Observe that we have taken a false hypothesis and deduced a true conclusion. Thus the third row of the table agrees with the usual intuitive understanding of the term implication.

Theorem b   If $1 = 3$, then $2 = 6$.

Proof: $1 = 3$ Hypothesis
$1 = 3$ Hypothesis
∴. $2 = 6$ Addition is well defined (equals added to equals)

Here we have taken a false hypothesis and deduced a false conclusion. Thus the fourth row of the table agrees with the usual intuitive understanding.

Example a   The following are translations of the statements that are grouped together.

(a) If it is raining, then the grass is wet.
Rain is sufficient reason for the grass to be wet.
A necessary condition for rain is that the grass be wet.
The grass is wet when it is raining.
It rains only if the grass is wet.

(b) Triangles have three sides.

   If a closed straight line figure is a triangle, then it has
     three sides.

   For a closed straight line figure to be a triangle, it is
     necessary that it have three sides.

   A sufficient condition for three sides is that the closed
     straight line figure be a triangle.

The reader should observe that $p \Rightarrow q$ gives the O_4 column and
$q \Rightarrow p$ gives the O_3 column.

EXERCISES (§ 3 · C)

1. Express the following statements as equivalent expressions
that employ the terms "if..., then...," "necessary," "sufficient,"
"implies," and "only if."

(a) If a series converges, then the general term tends to zero.

(b) Integers are rational numbers.

(c) A necessary condition for parallelism is that the lines never meet.

(d) For the function to be differentiable, it is necessary that the function be continuous.

(e) A positive integer will be divisible by an integer different from itself and one unless it is prime.

2. Establish statement variables for the various statements and
express the following in symbols.

(a) A rational number is expressible as the quotient of two integers.

(b) If a triangle is equilateral, then all three of its sides are congruent.

(c) A square is necessarily a rectangle.

(d) A sufficient condition for a triangle to be equiangular is that it be
equilateral.

(e) When the sides of a rectangle are equal, it is a square.

(f) A rhombus with right angles must be a square.

(g) All rectangles are quadrangles.

3. Establish statement variables for the various statements and express the following in symbols. Describe the conditions or actions that would break the promise or break the rule.

(a) Jack promised Mary the following: "I will take you on a picnic Sunday unless it is raining."

(b) You may open the darkroom door except when the "in use" light is on.

3·D   Biconditional

Second to implication in importance to mathematics is the biconditional operator. It is denoted by $<\Longrightarrow>$ and it is read "if and only if." The basic concept is: it is the conjunction of "p if q" and "p only if q," and its symbol is simply a combination of $p \Longrightarrow q$ and $q \Longrightarrow p$. Since the general techniques of truth table construction are given in Chapter 2, it is a little premature to develop a truth table now. But the construction is as follows:

p	q	$p \Longrightarrow q$	$q \Longrightarrow p$	$(p \Longrightarrow q) \wedge (q \Longrightarrow p)$
T	T	T	T	T
T	F	F	T	F
F	T	T	F	F
F	F	T	T	T

The reader might defer the study of this until the later section, but it is included here to indicate its development. Notice that the final column is the operator O_7, so formally we take the following definition.

Definition 8:

p	q	$p <\Longrightarrow> q$
T	T	T
T	F	F
F	T	F
F	F	T

There are three important ways for expressing the biconditional in mathematics. They are:

> p if and only if q.
> p is a necessary and sufficient condition for q.
> A necessary and sufficient condition for q is p.

The proof of a theorem stated in this fashion usually requires two proofs. Namely, p implies q and q implies p. The theorem p implies q is called the "only if" part or the "sufficiency." The theorem q implies p is called the "if" part or the "necessity." For convenience the reader might refer to the table and example.

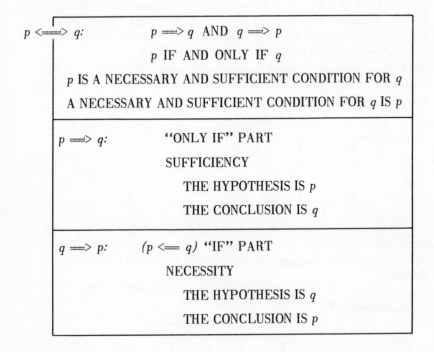

We will have occasion to include theorem and proofs in the exercises and examples. Theorems are generally expressed as implications, and a proof procedure is an orderly array of deductive conclusions drawn from generally known results in the system used. This is illustrated in Example b. Here the general setting is plane geometry and the discussion is expressed in a sequence of steps that should be apparent to anyone familiar with the elementary concepts of plane geometry. In a formal system, the postulates and definitions are precisely stated. Then the theorems should be listed and precisely stated. In such a formal setting, there should never be any doubt about precisely what postulates are assumed and what theorems are used to reach the conclusions in the various steps. We will have occasion to include both informal and formal proofs in the explanation of the material. Most of the examples will be from various mathematical disciplines, and we will assume that the reader is familiar with subjects like plane geometry and elementary algebra. The formal proofs will be in a system for the ordered real numbers. This system with its postulates, definitions, notation, and selected theorems is given in the appendix. Such a formal proof is given in Example c.

Example b. In a triangle the base angles are congruent if and only if the triangle is isosceles. (See figure 1.)

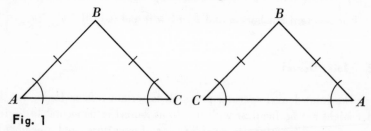

Fig. 1

(In a triangle a necessary and sufficient condition for the triangle to be isosceles is that the base angles be congruent.) In this example an isosceles triangle is defined as one in which two sides are congruent.

Proof: "if" part (necessity)

Our hypothesis is that triangle ABC is isosceles. Thus sides AB and BC are congruent, and triangles ABC and CBA are congruent by the side-angle-side statement from plane geometry. Hence the corresponding angles BAC and BCA are congruent.

"only if" part (sufficiency)
Our hypothesis is that angles BAC and BCA are congruent. Note that side AC is congruent to side CA. So, the triangles ABC and CBA are congruent by the angle-side-angle theorem from plane geometry. Therefore the corresponding sides AB and CB are congruent.

Example c. It occasionally happens that an "if and only if" theorem is so simple that one can prove "both" parts at once. This is a rare occurrence, but the following is included as an example of such a proof. Here "iff" is used as an abbreviation for "if and only if." It is a formal proof from the ordered real number system, as given in the Appendix.

For two real numbers a and b, $a < b$ if and only if $^-b, < {}^-a$.

Proof: $a < b$ iff $a + ({}^-a + {}^-b) < b + ({}^-a + {}^-b)$ $O\,3$ and T7*

iff $a + ({}^-a + {}^-b) < b + ({}^-b + {}^-a)$ $A\,5$

iff $(a + {}^-a) + {}^-b < (b + {}^-b) + {}^-a$ $A\,2$

iff $0 + {}^-b < 0 + {}^-a$ $A\,4$

iff ${}^-b < {}^-a$ $A\,3$

EXERCISES (§ 3 · D)

1. Give a formal proof (like Example c) for the following theorem.

For two real numbers a and b, $a > b$ if and only if ${}^-b > {}^-a$.

3 · E   Joint Denial

The joint denial operator plays an important role in logic, but the reader might not be familiar with it. Joint denial is important to logic since it forms a functionally complete set of operators, and a number of formal systems use it as their primitive operator. Functional completeness need not concern us here. So, we add joint denial to our collection for the purpose of having an operator for O_{12}. Its English equivalent is "neither p nor q" and its notation is the vertical arrow whose head points down. The reader might observe that it is the negation of weak disjunction.

Definition 9:

p	q	$p \downarrow q$
T	T	F
T	F	F
F	T	F
F	F	T

---

*   See Appendix.

3·F   Does Not Imply

In order to obtain an operator for each of the necessary truth table columns, we add one additional operator. It is "p does not imply q," and its notation is $\not\Rightarrow$ (the implication symbol with a slash mark through it). The reader might note that it is the negation of implication.

Definition 10:

p	q	$p \not\Rightarrow q$
T	T	F
T	F	T
F	T	F
F	F	F

Now the table of possible binary operators is complete. The non-constant columns $O_2, O_3, \ldots O_{15}$ are respective $p \vee q$, $q \Rightarrow p$, $p \Rightarrow q$, p/q, p, $p \Longleftrightarrow q$, $\sim p$, q, $\sim q$, $p \veebar q$, $p \downarrow q$, $q \not\Rightarrow p$, $p \not\Rightarrow q$, $p \wedge q$.

EXERCISES (§ 3 · F)

1. Use the following statement variables to indicate the expressions below. Then write the listed statements in symbols, using the proper operators.

> p: $a < b$
> q: $b > c$
> r: $a < c$
> s: $a = c$

(a) If $a < b$ or $b > c$, then $a < c$.

(b) It is not the case that $a < b$ and $a < c$ if and only if it is not the case that $b > c$.

(c) If $a < c$ and $b > c$, then $a < b$.

(d) $a < c$ or $a < b$, but not both.

(e) It is the case that $a < b$ or it is the case that $a < c$, but surely it is not the case that $a < b$ and $a < c$.

(f) Neither $a < b$ nor $b > c$.

(g) $a \leq c$

(h) $a < c$ or $a = c$.

(i) If $a = c$ and $a < b$, then $b > c$.

2. A restaurant invites the customers to enjoy their extra special bread with the directions: "Slice the hot loaf, don't spare the butter; or take it home later."

(a) May you take the bread home later?

(b) May you take the butter home later?

Chapter 2

FORMULAS AND TRUTH TABLES

We are interested in a general technique that will generate a truth table for any formula. A formula is any correct finite combination of statement variables and operators, i.e., an expression formed according to the following definition.

Definition 1: An expression is a *formula* if and only if it is a statement variable or it is arrived at by a finite number of applications of the following steps:

(i) $\sim f$, where f is a formula

(ii) $f \theta g$, where f and g are each formulas and θ is one of the binary operators defined in Chapter 1, §3.*

§1 PUNCTUATION

Grouping indicators are needed to give meaning to formulas. For example $p \wedge q \vee r$ is meaningless unless the reader understands whether we mean $(p \wedge q) \vee r$ or $p \wedge (q \wedge r)$.† Up to this point we have used parentheses to indicate the proper grouping and now we further explain their use.

Parentheses are used to indicate the scope of an operator. Brackets, [ ], and braces, { }, may be used for variety or emphasis, but they are not necessary. Any parenthesis grouping requires both a left parenthesis, "(," and a right parenthesis, ")," and the scope is indicated with the combined pair. Thus a binary operator joins the two

---

*   The usual expression is well formed formula (w.f.f.). The reader might find the game *Wff 'N Proof* interesting.

†   In ordinary written discourse the comma is usually used to distinguish between the two, that is, "*p* and *q*, or *r*" and "*p*, and *q* or *r*." In ordinary verbal discourse the pause is used, that is, "*p* and *q* ... or *r*" and "*p* ... and *q* or *r*."

indicated groupings and a unary operator operates on the immediately following expression. Consider the following example, $\{p \wedge [(q \vee r) \downarrow s]\} / t$. The disjunction operates on the q and the r. The parentheses group the $q \vee r$ together before the arrow, so the $\downarrow$ operates on the $(q \vee r)$ and the s. The conjunction joins the p and the bracketed expression, and the stroke joins the expression in the braces with the t.*

For the unary operator negation, the tilde operates on the statement variable or on the parenthesis group that immediately follows. In $\sim(p \vee \sim q) / t$, the first negation operates on the whole expression $(p \vee \sim q)$ and the second negation operates only on the q.

§2 TRUTH TABLES FOR A GIVEN FORMULA

A formula is an expression that is fundamentally statement variables on which operators operate for a finite number of times. Consequently, the formula's truth value is determined by a finite number of decisions based on the definition of the operators. For example $\tau((p \vee q) \Longrightarrow p)$ when $\tau(p) = F$, $\tau(q) = T$ is found by the following sequence of steps.

$$\tau(p \vee q) = T \text{ by Definition 4 in Chapter 1}$$

$$\tau((p \vee q) \Longrightarrow p) = F \text{ by Definition 7 in Chapter 1}$$

The truth table for the formula requires the truth value of the formula for all possible assignments of truth values to the statement variable components. This introduces the problem of determining the number of rows for the table given the number of different statement variables present in the formula. When there are two statement variables present, for example, p and q, the table will have four rows. The reason is that there are two possible truth values, T or F,

---

* Occasionally the parentheses are omitted when an associative operator is used. That is, when any interpretation will be an equivalent expression. See Chapter 3, §1. In the algebra of real numbers, the reader is used to the expression $x + y + z$. Because addition is an associative operator, the parentheses are omitted. But the expression $x \div y \div z$ is ambiguous unless there is some hierarchy convention agreed upon by the persons communicating. Note that in general $x \div (y \div z)$ is not equal to $(x \div y) \div z$.

for p and two for q. Hence four possible combinations of truth value for p and q. These are T, T; T, F; F, T; and F, F. The full table for the previous example is:

p	q	$p \vee q$	$(p \vee q) \Longrightarrow p$
T	T	T	T
T	F	T	T
F	T	T	F
F	F	F	T

The number of rows in a truth table is always established by the number of distinct statement variables present in the formula. In the above discussion we noted that a formula with two statement variables present would have a truth table with four rows. In case there are three statement variables present, p, q, r, then there would be two possible truth values for each of the components. That is p could be either T or F, q could be T or F, and r could be T or F. These three independent dual choices yields $2 \cdot 2 \cdot 2$ or 8 possible combinations. Any complete arrangement would be correct, but we select the first of the following to maintain a fixed orderly arrangement. The second arrangement is also widely used.

p	q	r		p	q	r		p	q	r
T	T	T		T	T	T		F	F	T
T	T	F		F	T	T		F	T	T
T	F	T		T	F	T		T	F	F
T	F	F		F	F	T		T	T	T
F	T	T		T	T	F		F	F	F
F	T	F		F	T	F		T	F	T
F	F	T		T	F	F		F	T	F
F	F	F		F	F	F		T	T	F

A formula with n distinct statement variables would have 2^n rows in its truth table. That is, there would be a dual choice for the truth value of each of the n statement variables and this would give $2 \cdot 2 \cdots 2$ or 2^n rows in the table.

A truth table for any formula requires a finite number of decisions and given sufficient time the table may be constructed. In fact a formula with n distinct statement variables and k operators will require $k \cdot 2^n$ decisions. By the above discussion, there will be 2^n rows and each of

27

the k operators would have one column of 2^n decisions to make. Hence $k \cdot 2^n$ decisions in all. With practice we do not need to constantly refer to the definition tables, but it is still not a pleasant or challenging task to construct a large table.

Whenever the truth table is constructed by a sequence of steps with each step incorporating one operator, the technique is referred to as the *matrix method*.

Example a   A matrix method table for
$$(((s \vee t) \implies s) \vee p) \iff (p \vee q).$$
There are four statement variable components: $p, q, s, t,$ and thus 2^4 or sixteen rows in the table.

p	q	s	t	$s \vee t$	$(s \vee t)$ $\implies s$	$((s \vee t)$ $\implies s) \vee p$	$p \vee q$	$(((s \vee t) \implies s)$ $\vee p) \iff (p \vee q)$
T	T	T	T	T	T	T	T	T
T	T	T	F	T	T	T	T	T
T	T	F	T	T	F	T	T	T
T	T	F	F	F	T	T	T	T
T	F	T	T	T	T	T	T	T
T	F	T	F	T	T	T	T	T
T	F	F	T	T	F	T	T	T
T	F	F	F	F	T	T	T	T
F	T	T	T	T	T	T	T	T
F	T	T	F	T	T	T	T	T
F	T	F	T	T	F	F	T	F
F	T	F	F	F	T	T	T	T
F	F	T	T	T	T	T	F	F
F	F	T	F	T	T	T	F	F
F	F	F	T	T	F	F	F	T
F	F	F	F	F	T	T	F	F

Occasionally it is convenient to arrange the truth table in a blended or messy fashion. The reason for this is that considerable time is saved in writing out the parts.

Example b   A blended matrix method truth table

$((((p$	$\underline{\vee}$	$q)$	$/$	$p)$	$\wedge$	$q)$	$\downarrow$	$p)$	$\wedge$	q
T	F	T	T	T	T	T	F	T	F	T
T	T	F	F	T	F	F	F	T	F	F
F	T	T	T	F	T	T	F	F	F	T
F	F	F	T	F	F	F	T	F	F	F

STEP: 1 2 1   3 1   4 1   5 1   6 1

The columns of possible truth values are placed under the statement variables (step 1), then the values are established by the operators that combine two statement variables (step 2). In this example step 2 has only one column, but it may be more than one in other problems. For example, $(p \vee q) / (p \downarrow q)$ would have four rows, four columns to list in the first step and two columns to list in the second step. These two columns would be under the $\vee$ and the $\downarrow$. After step two, successive steps generate the other two columns (steps 3, 4, 5, 6) and the final column of values is obtained. Occasionally the final column is circled for convenience or later reference, and most of the time the steps are not numbered. They are numbered here to aid the explanation.

EXERCISES (§ 2.)

1. Which of the following are formulas?

(a) p,

(b) p_{12345},

(c) $pq \vee s$,

(d) dog,

(e) $p \vee q \wedge s$,

(f) $(p \wedge q) \vee s$,

(g) George Washington rode a white horse on January 1, 1776.

2. Determine how many different expressions might be generated from $p \wedge q \wedge r \implies s \wedge t$ by inserting parentheses.

3. Find the truth tables.

(a) $(p \underline{\vee} p) \wedge q$

(b) $p \Longleftrightarrow (q \Longrightarrow p)$

(c) $p \downarrow p$

(d) $(p \lor q) \Longleftrightarrow (q \lor p)$

(e) $(p \land (q \land r)) \Longleftrightarrow ((p \land q) \land r)$

(f) $((p \land q) \lor (q \land r)) \Longrightarrow (p/s)$

4. Find the truth tables.

(a) $(p/p) \lor p$

(b) $(p \lor q)/(q \lor p)$

(c) $((p \Longrightarrow q) \land (q \Longrightarrow p)) \Longleftrightarrow (p \Longleftrightarrow q)$

(d) $((p \lor q) \lor r) \lor ((s \lor t) \lor p)$

(e) $(p/q)/r$

(f) $((p/q) \land (q/r)) \land (p/r)$

(g) $((p \lor q) \Longrightarrow r) \Longleftrightarrow ((p \Longrightarrow r) \land (q \Longrightarrow r))$

(h) $((p \land q) \Longrightarrow r) \Longleftrightarrow ((p \Longrightarrow r) \lor (q \Longrightarrow r))$

(i) $(p \land (\sim q \land \sim r) \lor ((\sim p \land (q \land \sim r)) \lor ((\sim p \land \sim q \land r)))$

5.

(a) Symbolize the expression "coffee, tea, or milk."

(b) Explain why the common restaurant menu meaning is given by 4(f) and not by 4(e).

6. Symbolize the expression for at most one of the four p, q, r, or s.

7. An unusual technique for dealing with truth value is given in J. F. Randolph's article "Cross-examining Propositional Calculus and Set Operations" *American Mathematical Monthly*, Vol. 72 (1965) pp. 117-127. Read the article and apply the techniques to the formulas given in Exercise 3.

8. Explain why the symbol expression for exactly one of three is given by $(p \land (q \downarrow r)) \underline{\lor} (\sim p \land (q \underline{\lor} r))$ and not by $(p \underline{\lor} q) \lor r$.

9. Symbolize the expression for exactly one of the four p, q, r, or s.

10. Verify that $(((p \mathbin{/} q) \wedge (p \mathbin{/} r)) \wedge (q \mathbin{/} r)) \wedge (p \vee (q \vee r))$ is a valid symbolization of exactly one of p, q, or r.

11. An interesting problem is the construction of a formula for a specified truth table. One method is given by listing the true situations with interconnecting disjunctions. For example,

p	q	r	$F(p, q, r)$
T	T	T	F
T	T	F	T
T	F	T	F
T	F	F	F
F	T	T	F
F	T	F	T
F	F	T	T
F	F	F	F

A formula with the same truth values as the unspecified $F(p, q, r)$ is given by:

$$(((p \wedge q) \wedge \sim r) \vee ((\sim p \wedge q) \wedge \sim r)) \vee ((\sim p \wedge \sim q) \wedge r)$$

Explain why this technique generates a formula with the desired truth values.

12. Apply the technique of Exercise 11 to generate formulas with the truth values listed below. The listings are given with the standard assignments of truth values to p, q, r. That is $F(p, q, r)$ in Exercise 11 would be stated as $F(p, q, r)$: F T F F F T T F.

(a) $A(p, q, r)$: F F F T F F F F.

(b) $B(p, q, r)$: T F F F F F F T.

(c) $C(p, q, r)$: F T F T F F T T.

(d) $D(p, q, r)$: T T T F F T T T.

(e) $E(p, q, r, s)$: T F F F F T F F F T T F F F F T.

13. Another technique for generating a formula for a specified truth table is to break the table into groups of four rows and note a brief formula that gives the specified truth values in relationship to the last two

31

columns. Then precede these formulas with expressions that introduce the truth values of the earlier statement variable(s) and join the formulas with disjunctions. This method applied to $F(p, q, r)$ of Exercise 11 gives: $(p \wedge \sim(q \Longrightarrow r)) \vee (\sim p \wedge (q \vee r))$.

Explain why this technique generates a formula with the desired truth values and apply the technique to the truth values listed in Exercise 12.

§3 TAUTOLOGIES AND CONTRADICTORY FORMULAS

In the preceding exercises you might have observed that some formulas were "always true." That is, no matter what values the statement variable components have, the compound statement has truth value T. See §2, Exercise 3(d) and Exercise 4(a). This means that the statement is true as a consequence of its form alone. Needless to say, in the study of logic we are very interested in investigating and finding these types of statement forms.

> **Definition 2:** A formula whose truth value is T for all possible assignments of truth value to its statement variable components is a *tautology*.

At the other extreme we have certain formulas that are always false. See Example b and Exercise 3(a). Note that the negation of this type of formula gives a tautology.

> **Definition 3:** A formula whose truth value is F for all possible assignments of truth value to its statement variable components is a *contradictory formula*.

There are also the formulas that fail to have constant truth value. That is, for one assignment of truth values to the statement variable components, its truth value is T; and for some other assignment, its truth value is F. See §2, Exercise 3(b).

> **Definition 4:** A formula that is neither a tautology nor a contradictory formula is *synthetic*.

In regard to the constant columns in the possible truth tables of Chapter 1, §2 and §3, we see that the problem is not the generation of a tautology type of operator. But the real problem is investigating the other operators to see when their combinations generate a formula that has constant truth value. We could have named operators to correspond to O_1 and O_{16}, but they would have had no language equivalent. Also this would be in a direction opposite to our basic interest in generating tautologies.

Another major point in regard to formulas is their equivalence. Since we are interested in their truth value alone, we will say that two formulas are equivalent when they have the same corresponding truth values for corresponding assignments of truth value to their statement variable components. This concept requires that we indicate the statement variables that are used in a particular formula. So, $f(p_1, p_2, \ldots, p_n)$ will be used to indicate a formula that has the statement variables $p_1, p_2, \ldots, p_{n-1}$, and p_n as its statement variable components. For example $g(p, q, r, s)$ might represent $((p, \vee s) \downarrow (q \veebar p)) \, / \, r$.

Definition 5: Two formulas $f(p_1, \ldots, p_n)$ and $g(p_1, \ldots, p_n)$ are *logically equivalent*, $f \equiv g$, if and only if any assignment of truth values to $p_1 \ldots, p_n$ will generate identical truth values for the formulas $f(p_1, \ldots, p_n)$ and $g(p_1, \ldots, p_n)$.

The reader might observe that we could make the remark: $f \equiv g$ when and only when $f \Longleftrightarrow g$ is a tautology. So the new notation might seem redundant, but the equivalence relationship is used in this treatise as an emphasis of the idea of logical equivalence. That is, we would like to distinguish between logical equivalence and the biconditional operator. The biconditional operator appears in formulas, and the formulas may or may not be tautologies. The equivalence is a relation on formulas that states that the equivalent formulas are known to give identical truth values for like assignments of truth values to the variables.

The careful reader might also question the interplay of the "if and only if" expression, the biconditional operator, and logical equivalence. Especially when one is used to define the other. There is an involved question stated here, and a complete discussion is beyond the scope of this material. Remember that this treatise is an intuitive discussion of basic logic material related to mathematics.

It is intuitively clear that equivalent expressions may be substituted for one another. So, without any formal expansion on the subject, we accept the following rule of substitution: *In a formula, any part may be replaced by an equivalent expression: and the resulting formula is equivalent to the original formula.*

A very important problem in logic is the exercise of expressing one operator in terms of a given set of other operators. This is especially important in discussions that involve function completeness or the setting up of formal systems. For example, the reader has noted that joint denial and Sheffer stroke are negations of weak disjunction and conjunction respectively. It also happens that all the other operators can be expressed as combinations of negation and conjunction. The condition, $p \Rightarrow q$, is known to be false only when p is true and q is false. Thus we might suspect that $p \Rightarrow q$ and $\sim(p \wedge \sim q)$ are equivalent, and this is the case. It is simple to note this with a truth table — the biconditional, $p \Longleftrightarrow q$, is the conjunction of two conditionals, $p \Rightarrow q$ and $q \Rightarrow p$. But $(q \Rightarrow p) \equiv (\sim p \Rightarrow \sim q)$, so we have an equivalent expression for the biconditional that employs only the conjunction and negation operators, that is, $(p \Leftrightarrow q) \equiv (\sim(p \wedge \sim q) \wedge \sim(\sim p \wedge q))$. If we would continue this analysis we could eventually express each operation as an equivalent expression of negation and conjunction operations. This is detailed in Example c. This leads us to the remarkable conclusion that we could go about the business of daily communications using only "not" and "and." But this would be awkward as we can see when "fish or cut bait" is expressed as "it is not the case that one should not fish and one should not cut bail."

Example c   Each operator may be expressed in an equivalent fashion with only the use of negation and conjunction.

$$(p \vee q) \equiv \sim(\sim p \wedge \sim q)$$

$$(p \veebar q) \equiv \sim(\sim p \wedge \sim q) \wedge \sim(p \wedge q)$$

$$(p \Rightarrow q) \equiv \sim(p \wedge \sim q)$$

$$(p \Leftrightarrow q) \equiv \sim(p \wedge \sim q) \wedge \sim(\sim p \wedge q)$$

$$(p \downarrow q) \equiv \sim p \wedge \sim q$$

$$(p \,/\, q) \equiv \sim(p \wedge q)$$

Note that $(\sim p) \equiv (p \mid p)$ and $(p \wedge q) \equiv ((p \mid q) \mid (p \mid q))$. So we observe that we could arrive at all the operators in terms of simply the Sheffer stroke. That is, express the formula in terms of conjunction and negation and then use the above equivalences to substitute. For example $p \downarrow q$ is equivalent to $\sim p \wedge \sim q$, this is equivalent to $(\sim p \mid \sim q)$ $/(\sim p \mid \sim q)$ and this is equivalent to $((p \mid p) \mid (q \mid q)) \mid ((p \mid p) \mid (q \mid q))$. Needless to say this technique usually does not generate the shortest equivalent expression.

EXERCISES (§ 3.)

1. Classify the formulas in Section §2, Exercises 3 and 4.

2. For the fun of it (just to say you did) go through the chain of substitution that expresses strong disjunction in terms of the Sheffer stroke.

3. Try to find a short expression that expresses each operator in an equivalent fashion with only the Sheffer stroke.

4. Try to find a short expression that expresses each operator in an equivalent fashion with only

(a) negation and implication

(b) joint denial

(c) negation and weak disjunction.

5. Try to find any other single operator (other than Sheffer stroke and joint denial) that is such that the other operators may be expressed in terms of it.

6. Try to find any set of two operators (other than negation, weak disjunction; negation, conjunction; negation, implication) that are such that the other operators may be expressed in terms of them.

7. Combine the results of the six preceding exercises in chart form, as shown.

		~ ∧	~∨	~=>	/	↓
$p \wedge q$	$\equiv$	✕			$((p/q)/(p/q))$	
$p \vee q$	$\equiv$	$\sim(\sim p \wedge \sim q)$	✕			
$p \veebar q$	$\equiv$	$\sim(\sim p \wedge \sim q) \wedge \sim(p \wedge q)$				
$p \Rightarrow q$	$\equiv$	$\sim(p \wedge \sim q)$		✕		
$p \Leftrightarrow q$	$\equiv$	$\sim(p \wedge \sim q) \wedge \sim(\sim p \wedge q)$				
$p \downarrow q$	$\equiv$	$\sim p \wedge \sim q$				✕
$\sim p$	$\equiv$	✕	✕	✕	p / p	
p / q	$\equiv$	$\sim(p \wedge q)$				

8. Verify the following tautologies.

(a) Law of Detachment $\qquad (p \wedge (p \Rightarrow q)) \Rightarrow q$

(b) *Modus tollendo tollens* $\qquad (\sim q \wedge (p \Rightarrow q)) \Rightarrow \sim p$

(c) *Modus tollendo ponens* $\qquad (\sim p \wedge (p \vee q)) \Rightarrow q$

(d) Law of Simplification $\qquad (p \wedge q) \Rightarrow p$

(e) Law of Hypothetical Syllogism $\qquad ((p \Rightarrow q) \wedge (q \Rightarrow r)) \Rightarrow (p \Rightarrow r)$

(f) Law of Absurdity $\qquad (p \Rightarrow (q \wedge \sim q)) \Rightarrow \sim p$

(g) Law of Addition $\qquad p \Rightarrow (p \vee q)$

(h) Law of Double Negation $\qquad p \Leftrightarrow \sim \sim p$

(i) Law of Excluded Middle $\qquad p \vee \sim p$

(j) Law of Contradiction $\qquad \sim(p \wedge \sim p)$

9. Verify that any statement variable formula utilizing two statement variables is equivalent to a statement variable formula with at most three symbols. Illustrate this by finding the operators θ in the following equivalences.

(a) $(((p / q) \downarrow (q \Rightarrow p)) \Leftrightarrow (\sim q \veebar p)) \equiv (p \; \theta q)$

(b) $((p \veebar q) \wedge (p \Leftrightarrow q)) \equiv (p \; \theta \; p)$

(c) $((p \vee q) \vee (p / q)) \equiv (p \; \theta \; p)$

§4 THE INDIRECT METHOD

The preceding matrix truth tables in §2 show an effective technique for deciding whether a formula is tautological, synthetic, or contradictory. It is a mechanical technique that requires minimum reasoning ability and maximum labor. So we are motivated to search for another method. This leads us to the indirect method which is considerably faster and less tedious in many cases.

The basic idea of the indirect method is to show that is is impossible for the formula to be anything else. That is, any assumption that is opposed to the desired classification must lead to a contradiction. This backwards approach is in a sense opposite from the usual direction of a proving method, hence the term "indirect."

When the indirect method is used to demonstrate that a formula is a tautology, the original assumption is that the formula is false. This information is used through a series of steps to arrive at a contradiction. That is, it is impossible for the formula to be false; so it is always true. In Example d the first step is to assume that it is possible for the formula to be false. The question mark indicates that this is a temporary assumption. Since the main operator is an implication, there is only one way for the formula to be false. The hypothesis, $(p \wedge q) \vee (\sim p \wedge q)$, must be true: and the conclusion, q, must be false. This is indicated with the flow arrows, and the lines indicate the scope of the truth values. Now transfer the truth value of q to the left side as indicated with flow arrow. The conjunction establishes the next truth value without information about p. The steps continue until the contradiction is reached. Namely that the truth value of the hypothesis is T and F, an impossibility.

Example d

$$((p \wedge q) \ \vee \ (\sim p \wedge q)) \Longrightarrow q$$

37

A formula may also be shown to be contradictory by use of the indirect method. Here the technique is to show that the assumption, the formula has truth value T, leads to a contradiction. Hence the formula has constant truth value of F, and it is contradictory.

Example e

$$((p \downarrow q) \lor p) \downarrow (p \,/\, q)$$

T	T	T	←	←
↓	↓	T	T	
F	T	↑	↑	
↓	T	T		
T	↑	↑		
F	F			
↑	T(?)	↑		

If it happens that neither assumption leads to a contradiction, then the formula is synthetic. That is, if it is possible for it to take on the truth values T and F, then its classification is synthetic.

The indirect method works best when you have few cases to worry about. An example of this is testing a formula to decide if it is a tautology when its primary operator is implication. This makes the indirect method a very useful technique in mathematics, primarily because we are interested in tautologies, and implication is the most widely used operator in mathematics. To further illustrate this, we include Example f.

Example f

$$((p \land q) \implies r) \implies (p \implies (q \Rightarrow r))$$

5	T	T	F	←	←	←	
	↓	↓	T	T	F		4
6	T	F	↑	↑	↑		
	↓	T	F			3	
7	F	↑	↑				
	T	F			2		
	↑	F(?)	↑			step 1	

38

First assume that the formula is false. There is only one way that it can be false, and that is for the left half to be true and the right half to be false (step 2). But step three gives p the truth value T and $q \Rightarrow r$ the truth value F. Step four says that q must be T and r must be F. Now apply these requirements to the left half. Therefore, step six gives an implication with T as the hypothesis and F as the conclusion. Now, step seven says that its truth value is F and this contradicts the fact that it must be T. It is impossible for the formula to be F; so, it must always be T, that is, a tautology. Note that in each step there was no choice; the truth values of the components are uniquely determined.

Example g

$$(\; p \; \underline{\vee} \; q \;) \quad \Longleftrightarrow \quad (\; q \; \underline{\vee} \; p \;)$$

Case 1a

T	T		←	←
↓			T	T
F			↑	↑
T			F	
↑	F(?)		↑	

Case 1b

F	F		←	←
↓			F	F
F			↑	↑
T			F	
↑	F(?)		↑	

Case 2a

F	T		←	←
↓			T	F
T			↑	↑
F			T	
↑	F(?)		↑	

Example g (continued)

Case 2b	T	T		←	←
	↓			F	T
	T			↑	↑
	F				T
	↑	F(?)			↑

Example g is included to illustrate that the indirect method will not always save time. In this situation there are too many alternate cases. First of all, when we assume that the whole formula is false, we see that there are two ways, case 1 or case 2, for this to happen. Then for each of the two cases we have two more cases, parts a or b, for the exclusive disjunction. In the final result we would have been better off with a truth table.

The reader might observe that the indirect method is generally an individual test. That is, it is useful when you want to decide about a certain formula for yourself. If you want to write a proof about a tautology, it is difficult to indicate clearly the sequence of steps.

One final word about this method. Before you conclude that you have a contradiction, *make sure that you have considered all the possibilities!*

EXERCISES (§ 4)

1. Show by the indirect method that the following are tautologies.

(a) $((p => q) \land \sim q) => \sim p$

(b) $((p \Rightarrow q) \land (q \Rightarrow r)) => (p \Rightarrow r)$

(c) $((p => (q => r)) => ((p => q) => (p => r))$

(d) $(p \land q) => (p \Rightarrow q)$

(e) $(p \land (q \lor r)) <\!\!=\!\!\!=\!\!> ((p \land q) \lor (p \land r))$

(f) $(p => q) <\!\!=\!\!\!=\!\!> (\sim q \Rightarrow \sim p)$

(g) $((p \downarrow q) \land (s \lor p)) / ((p / s) => (p \land q)$

§5 ALTERNATE SYSTEMS OF PUNCTUATION

In some texts the dot notation is used to indicate the scope of an operator. The basic technique is simply explained with the following convention. *The scope of an operator will extend backward past a fewer number of dots and forward to a larger number of dots.* The dots on the left side of the operator are compared with the ones on the right side of operators that precede it, and the dots on the right side of the operator are compared with the ones on the left side of operators that follow it. This additional convention reduces the punctuation symbols.

Example h

1. $p \lor q \cdot / r$ means $(p \lor q) / r$

$p \lor q \cdot / : r \lor p \cdot / s$

means

$(p \lor q) / ((r \lor p) / s)$

Some systems further complicate the problem by using dots for conjunction and punctuation. When this happens, a further convention is usually agreed upon. Dots used to punctuate will extend past an equal number of dots used to conjoin and the scope of a single dot used to conjoin will be wider than that of any unpunctuated operator. Note that in some sense a conjunction dot is half operator and half punctuation symbol. Unless a tilde is dotted, it negates only the following statement variable.

Example i

$p \lor q \cdot r$ would be $((p \lor q) \cdot r)$ or $((p \lor q) \land r)$

$p \lor \cdot q \cdot r$ would be $(p \lor (q \cdot r))$ or $(p \lor (q \land r))$

$p \lor : \cdot q : r \cdot s$ would be $p \lor (q \cdot (r \cdot s))$

$p \lor \cdot q \cdot r : s$ would be $(p \lor (q \cdot r)) \cdot s$

In other texts authors may establish a hierarchy of operators; that is the operators have certain strengths assigned to them. One system could be the following (i) bicondition is stronger than implication, (ii) implication is stronger than conjunction, (iii) conjunction is stronger than disjunction, and (iv) disjunction is stronger than negation. Unless it is otherwise indicated by means of parentheses, the scope of an operator will extend past any weaker operator. In this system we would have the following translations.

$p \Rightarrow q \Leftrightarrow p \wedge q \vee s$ would be $(p \Rightarrow q) \Leftrightarrow (p \wedge (q \vee s))$

$(p \Leftrightarrow q) \Rightarrow p \vee s \wedge t \Leftrightarrow \sim(s \vee t)$ would be

$$((p \Leftrightarrow q) \Rightarrow ((p \vee s) \wedge t)) \Leftrightarrow \sim(s \vee t)$$

The most interesting alternate system is one that uses no punctuation at all. The parenthesis-free notation was developed by the Polish logician J. Lukasiewicz, and it is often referred to as "the Polish notation." In this system each operator is assigned a capital letter to represent it; and instead of the operator being placed between the formulas, it is placed immediately to the left of the formulas that it operates on.

(i) Negation is associated with N

$\sim p$ as Np

(ii) Implication is associated with C

$p \Rightarrow q$ as Cpq

(iii) Conjunction is associated with K

$p \wedge q$ as Kpq

(iv) Disjunction is associated with A

$p \vee q$ as Apq

The operator may join only the two immediately following groups, so any formula may be written in an unambiguous fashion without punctuation marks.

Example ¡ $p \Rightarrow (q \Rightarrow r)$ would be $CpCqr$

$(p \Rightarrow q) \Rightarrow r$ would be $CCpqr$

$((p \Rightarrow q) \Rightarrow r) \Rightarrow s$ would be $CCCpgrs$

$(p \Rightarrow q) \Rightarrow (r \Rightarrow s)$ would be $CCpqCrs$

$(p \wedge q) \vee (s \Rightarrow t)$ would be $AKpqCst$

Example j (continued)

$p \wedge ((p \wedge p) \wedge p)$ would be $KpKKppp$

$p \wedge (p \wedge (p \wedge p))$ would be $KpKpKpp$

In the hierarchy notation any extensive development would be extremely awkward to use, but certain simple adaptations are commonly used. In fact the reader probably has started thinking in terms of biconditional being somewhat "stronger" than conjunction. So in simple structures, the system can be quite natural. The Polish system is a little unusual to use, but it is important to some of the computer systems in present use.

In our system we will use parentheses, and the only hierarchy convention that we accept will be the one stated about negation in §1.

Chapter 3

ALGEBRA OF STATEMENTS

Any study of operators should include an investigation into their algebraic structure. So we now investigate standard algebraic relationships and use this study to obtain practice in the use of the logical symbols.

The standard relationships are those basic to the algebra of the real numbers. These are the associative laws, commutative laws, distributive laws and the negation relationships.

§1 THE ASSOCIATIVE LAWS

Definition 1: In general, a binary operator θ is termed *associative* if and only if for all operands p, q, r: $p \ \theta \ (q \ \theta \ r)$ is equivalent to $(p \ \theta \ q) \ \theta \ r$.*

We recall that both addition and multiplication are associative operators in the algebra of real numbers, and subtraction and division are not associative operators. That is, for all real numbers a, b, c:

$$a + (b + c) = (a + b) + c$$
$$a \cdot (b \cdot c) = (a \cdot b) \cdot c$$

But, for real numbers a, b, and c:

$$a - (b - c) \text{ might not equal } (a - b) - c$$
$$a \div (b \div c) \text{ might not equal } (a \div b) \div c$$

---

* An *operand* is an object(s) that an operator is able to operate on.

Theorem a   Inclusive disjunction is an associative operator.

$(p$	$\vee$	$(q$	$\vee$	$r))$	$\equiv$	$((p$	$\vee$	$q)$	$\vee$	$r)$
T	T	T	T	T		T	T	T	T	T
T	T	T	T	F		T	T	T	T	F
T	T	F	T	T		T	T	F	T	T
T	T	F	F	F		T	T	F	T	F
F	T	T	T	T		F	T	T	T	T
F	T	T	T	F		F	T	T	T	F
F	T	F	T	T		F	F	F	T	T
F	F	F	F	F		F	F	F	F	F

EXERCISES (§ 1)

1. Determine if the following are associative or nonassociative operators.

(a) conjunction

(b) exclusive disjunction

(c) if and only if

(d) implication

(e) Sheffer stroke

(f) joint denial

§ 2   THE COMMUTATIVE LAWS

Definition 2:   In general, a binary operation θ is termed *commutative* if and only if for all operands p, q:

$p \ \theta \ q$ is equivalent to $q \ \theta \ p$.

We again recall that addition and multiplication are also commutative operators for real numbers, but subtraction and division are not. that is, for all real numbers a and b:

$$a + b = b + a$$

$$a \cdot b = b \cdot a$$

45

But for real numbers a and b:

$a - b$ might not equal $b - a$

$a \div b$ might not equal $b \div a$

Theorem b   Conjunction is a commutative operator.

($p \land q$)			=======	($q \land p$)		
T	T	T		T	T	T
T	F	F		F	F	T
F	F	T		T	F	F
F	F	F		F	F	F

EXERCISES (§2.)

1. Determine if the following are commutative or noncommutative operators.

(a) inclusive disjunction

(b) exclusive disjunction

(c) if and only if

(d) Sheffer stroke

(e) joint denial

(f) implication

§3   THE DISTRIBUTIVE LAWS

Definition 3: A binary operator θ is said to *distribute across* the binary operator Φ if and only if for all operands p, q, r:

$p \; \theta \; (q \; \Phi \; r)$ is equivalent to $(p \; \theta \; q) \; \Phi \; (p \; \theta \; r)$.

Again recall the binary operators in the algebra of the real numbers. Here multiplication distributes across addition, but addition does not distribute across multiplication. In symbols, this means, for real numbers a, b, c:

$$a \cdot (b + c) = (a \cdot b) + (a \cdot c)$$

but, $a + (b \cdot c)$ might not equal $(a + b) \cdot (a + c)$

Theorem c   Conjunction distributes across inclusive disjunction.

```
( p ∧ ( q ∨ r ))  ≡≡≡  (( p ∧ q )  ∨  ( p ∧ r ))
  T T   T T T           T T T    T    T T T
  T T   T T F           T T T    T    T F F
  T T   F T T           T F F    T    T T T
  T F   F F F           T F F    F    T F F
  F F   T T T           F F T    F    F F T
  F F   T T F           F F T    F    F F F
  F F   F T T           F F F    F    F F T
  F F   F F F           F F F    F    F F F
```

Example a   Conjunction does not distribute across implication.

```
( p ∧ ( q => r ))  ≢  (( p ∧ q )  =>  ( p ∧ r ))
  T T   T T T            T T T    T    T T T
  T F   T F F            T T T    F    T F F
  T T   F T T            T F F    T    T T T
  T T   F T F            T F F    T    T F F
  F F   T T T            F F T    T    F F T
  F F   T F F            F F T    T    F F F
  F F   F T T            F F F    T    F F T
  F F   F T F            F F F    T    F F F
```

The symbol $\not\equiv$ is used to indicate that two formulas are not equivalent.

Example b   The truth tables are left for the reader.

(a) implication distributes across disjunction.

$$(p => (q \land r)) \equiv ((p => q) \land (p => r))$$

(b) Sheffer stroke does not distribute across joint denial.

$$(p \,/\, (q \downarrow r)) \not\equiv ((p \,/\, q) \downarrow (p \,/\, r))$$

EXERCISES (§3.)

1. Show that inclusive disjunction distributes across conjunction.

2. Show that implication distributes across bicondition.

3. Even though it is odd to ask if an operator distributes across itself, it is a correct question according to our Definition 3.

(a) Show that strong disjunction does not distribute across strong disjunction.

(b) Show that implication distributes across implication.

4.

(a) Write out the expressions and explain the difference between (i) an operator being associative and (ii) an operator distributing across itself.

(b) Find two examples of operators that are associative and distributive across themselves.

(c) Find two examples of operators that are associative and do not distribute across themselves.

(d) Find an example of an operator that is not associative and does distribute across itself.

(e) Find two examples of operators that are not associative and do not distribute across themselves.

5. For any two real numbers x and y define the operation $x \circ y = x + y - xy$. Show that the circle operator on the real numbers:

(a) is associative.

(b) is commutative.

(c) does not distribute over addition.

(d) does not distribute over multiplication.

(e) does not distribute over itself.

§4 THE NEGATION RELATIONSHIPS

In the algebra of the real numbers there is one unary operator. It is of course the negative operator, and there are many analogous relationships between the negative operator and the negation operator.

In the real numbers, the negative operator is a self-annihilating operator, that is, $-(-a) = a$; and the negation operator is self-annihilating also.

Theorem d $\quad \sim(\sim p) \equiv p$

$$
\begin{array}{ccc}
\text{T} & \text{F T} & \text{T} \\
\text{F} & \text{T F} & \text{F}
\end{array}
$$

When we consider the effect on real numbers of interaction of the negative operator and the addition or multiplication operators, the analogy breaks down. That is, for real numbers

$$- (a + b) = (-a) + (-b)$$

$$- (ab) = (-a)(b) = a(-b)$$

But in logic we have the DeMorgan Laws, and they do not completely parallel the above.

The DeMorgan Laws state that the negation of a conjunction (disjunction) is the disjunction (conjunction) of the negations, that is,

$$\sim(p \wedge q) \equiv\equiv\equiv (\sim p \vee \sim q)$$

$$\sim(p \vee q) \equiv\equiv\equiv (\sim p \wedge \sim q)$$

In statements we have the following example. To say it is "not both raining and snowing;" we could say that "either it is not raining or it is not snowing."

Theorem e $\quad$ A DeMorgan Law

$\sim$	$(p$	$\wedge$	$q)$	$\equiv\equiv\equiv$	$\sim$	p	$\vee$	$\sim$	q
F	T	T	T		F	T	F	F	T
T	T	F	F		F	T	T	T	F
T	F	F	T		T	F	T	F	T
T	F	F	F		T	F	T	T	F

EXERCISES (§ 4.)

1. Prove the other DeMorgan Law

$$\sim(p \lor q) \ \equiv \ \sim p \land \sim q$$

2. Determine a type of "DeMorgan relationship for exclusive disjunction, i.e., determine θ in the following relationship.

$$\sim(p \lor q) \ \equiv \ \sim p \ \theta \ \sim q$$

3. Combine the theorems about the algebra of statements in the two charts.

(a) The associative and commutative laws.

	associative	commutative
$\land$	yes	
$\lor$		
$\underline{\lor}$		
$<\!\Rightarrow$		
$\Rightarrow$		no
$/$		
$\downarrow$		

For example, the "yes" indicates that conjunction is an associative operator. The "no" indicates that implication is not commutative.

(b) The distributive laws.

	$\lor$	$\underline{\lor}$	$<\!\Longrightarrow$	$\Rightarrow$	$/$	$\downarrow$
$\land$						
$\lor$	yes					
$\underline{\lor}$						
$<\!\Longrightarrow$						
$\Rightarrow$						
$/$	no					
$\downarrow$						

For example, the "yes" indicates that inclusive disjunction distributes across conjunction, and the "no" indicates that Sheffer stroke does not

50

distribute across inclusive disjunction. Generally in tables of this type the vertically listed element is read first; then the horizontally listed element.

    4. Do the following equalities hold for all real numbers x and y? See Exercise 5, in Section 3.

(a) $x \circ (-y) = - (x \circ y)$?

(b) $(-x) \circ y = - (x \circ y)$?

Chapter 4

APPLICATIONS

The statement calculus has numerous applications and we will not attempt to give any extensive discussion here. We will restrict our attention to simple written arguments and changes in form that are important to mathematical proofs. The simple and sometimes nonsensical written arguments are investigated in order that the reader might have an opportunity to practice translating written discussions into symbols. The section on mathematical proofs is important to the mathematics student. Consequently, it should be studied in detail.

In the mathematics section we do not give a complete discussion, but we develop certain techniques and investigation procedures that can be extended and applied to many mathematical situations that the reader might encounter. A major extension of the material would include an investigation into the changes used in the heart of mathematical proofs. Our discussion is limited to the form of the stated theorem, but an investigation into the body of a mathematical proof uses the same techniques. Thus the reader will be prepared to investigate changes within the body of a proof by using the techniques that we arrive at in §2 of this chapter.

§1 ARGUMENTS

A verbalized or written argument has various characteristics. First of all, the person advancing the discussion gives a collection of information that the observer is supposed to agree with or accept as true statements. Then the originator of the argument deduces a conclusion that he feels to be a consequence of the information. The sentences that represent the stated facts or suppositions are referred to as the *conditions*, and the consequence is termed the *conclusion*. The total communication constitutes the *argument*, and the symbolic representation is the *argument form*.

We now establish the intuitive criteria for accepting an argument as valid or invalid. The first question is whether the stated conditions are consistent (or inconsistent). That is, we would not consider an argument to be valid when the assumed information contradicted itself. The conditions generally can be symbolized as combinations, expressed by logical operators, of certain statement variables that represent the basic statements present. The consistence of the conditions will be established by symbolizing the basic statements, expressing the conditions as statement variable formulas, conjoining the conditions together, and using truth tables to see if the expression is contradictory. When the given conditions are compatible, then we ask if the conclusion is a valid inference from the stated conditions; that is, by the techniques of the statement calculus, does it logically follow? This inference will be established with truth tables to see if the conditions imply the conclusion.

The expression "it logically follows" is perhaps the most abused and vague term in daily communications. To avoid any ambiguity, we now formalize our intuitive criteria in the following definitions.

> **Definition 1:** An *argument form* is a set of conditions $C_1, C_2, \ldots, C_n$ and a conclusion K. Each condition and the conclusion is a formula using the basic statement variables present.

> **Definition 2:** An argument form is *valid* if and only if $(C_1 \wedge C_2) \wedge \ldots \wedge C_n$ is not contradictory and $((C_1 \wedge C_2) \wedge \ldots \wedge C_n) \implies K$ is a tautology.

> **Definition 3:** An argument form has *contradictory premises* if and only if $(C_1 \wedge C_2) \wedge \ldots \wedge C_n$ is a contradictory statement formula.

> **Definition 4:** An argument form states an *improper conclusion* if and only if it is not contradictory and not valid, that is, $((C_1 \wedge C_2) \wedge \ldots \wedge C_n) \implies K$ is not a tautology.

An argument form may be invalid either by having a contradictory set of premises or by stating an improper conclusion.

To illustrate these concepts, we now give three examples. The respective arguments (a) state a valid argument, (b) state contradictory premises, and (c) state an improper conclusion.

Example a   Consider the following: When a baby is hungry, the baby cries. But, when he is not mad, he does not cry. Everyone knows that a mad baby has a red face. So, hungry babies have red faces.

The speaker states the conditions, and he wants you to agree with his conclusion about hungry babies having red faces. The basic statements in the arguments may be represented with the following symbols:

h: The baby is hungry.

c: The baby cries.

m: The baby is mad.

r: The baby has a red face.

The argument form of the story is seen to be:

$$
\begin{array}{lcl}
h & \Rightarrow & c \\
\sim m & \Rightarrow & \sim c \\
m & \Rightarrow & r \\
\hline
\therefore\ h & \Rightarrow & r
\end{array}
$$

The format that we use is simply the conditions listed above the line and the conclusion below the line preceeded by three dots that represent "therefore."

We now need to classify the argument form: It is easy to see that the statement $(h \Rightarrow c) \wedge (\sim m \Rightarrow \sim c) \wedge (m \Rightarrow r)$ is not contradictory. Likewise it is easy to see that the statement $((h \Rightarrow c) \wedge (\sim m \Rightarrow \sim c) \wedge (m \Rightarrow r)) \Rightarrow (h \Rightarrow r)$ is a tautology. Consequently we could conclude that the argument form is valid. If the reader will substitute the equivalent expression $c \Rightarrow m$ for $\sim m \Rightarrow \sim c$ the correctness of the conclusion will be obvious.

Example b   Taxes are sometimes interrelated when each tax is a deductible item on the other tax. That is in some problems you may have the following situation: If you know tax A, then compute tax B. But you need to know tax B before you can calculate tax A. You must calculate one tax or the other first. Thus figure out tax A.

The basic conditions are:

    a: You know tax A.

    b: You know tax B.

The argument form is:

$$a \Rightarrow b$$
$$b \Rightarrow a$$
$$\underline{a \lor b}$$
$$\therefore\ a$$

The conjunction of the conditions, $(a \Rightarrow b) \land (b \Rightarrow a) \land (a \lor b)$, is a contradictory statement formula. Thus the argument has contradictory assumptions, and we would not accept any conclusion that it tries to deduce. Unfortunately, the realization that there is no solution to the dilemma does not help the poor taxpayer.

Example c "Voters, we stand at the brink of a great disaster to our economy. Unless Smith is re-elected, we will lose the airbase. But Smith will win if and only if he has your support. When we save the base, Smith will be in office. So Smith will win!"

We make the following statement variable representations:

    w: Smith will win.

    s: Smith has the voters' support.

    a: The community keeps the airbase.

Now the argument form is:

$$\sim w \Rightarrow \sim a$$
$$w \Leftrightarrow s$$
$$\underline{a \Rightarrow w}$$
$$\therefore\ w$$

The conjunction of the conditions is not contradictory, but the conclusion is not implied by them. Note that $((\sim w \Rightarrow \sim a) \wedge (w \Leftrightarrow s) \wedge (a \Rightarrow w)) \Rightarrow w$ is synthetic.

EXERCISES (§1.)

1. You either putt or drive well. But of course it is impossible to do both. If your putting is bad, you get mad. Fortunately when you are mad, you drive well. It goes without saying that you cannot both putt and be mad. Thus you must putt well.

2. If a tennis game is in progress, either it is daytime or the lights are on. A game is going on. The lights are off. So it must be daytime.

3. The instructor assigns homework when and only when he lectures. If class is dismissed, there will not be any lectures. There won't be both class and homework, but there will be one or the other. Therefore we will have homework.

4. If it is warm, I will play golf. When I do not play golf, I do not exert energy. If it is cool, I will exert energy. Do I play golf?

5. If you win cash you will not be an amateur. But if you win the tournament, you will receive cash. If you post as an amateur, you must remain as an amateur. Therefore a pro must win the tournament.

6. The wedding will be in June or in December. It can not be at both times. If the wedding is in December, we can expect snow and surely snow would not happen during a June wedding. But if we do not have the wedding in December, it will be too hot. Hot weather would imply that the wedding will be in June. Therefore the wedding will be in June.

7. Can the argument in Exercise 5 conclude that:

(a) You are an amateur?

(b) That you will win cash?

§2 MATHEMATICAL PROOFS

The statement calculus is very useful in mathematical proofs. The usual employment is a simple substitution of an equivalent form. Simple changes are readily recognized, but occasionally a complex change is needed in order that the theorem might be more readily proved. Some proof techniques are widely applied and standard nomenclature is assigned, but there are many changes in form that are unnamed. Likewise an unusual substitution occasionally is needed to generate an ingenious proof. The problem is that most authors do not mention the changes, and they simply assume that the reader recognizes them as valid. Of course, this can be a real hardship on the student who is struggling to understand the proof. Hidden logic changes only complicate his problem. The main purpose of this section is to explain the standard changes and outline alternate techniques. The alternate techniques will include in their explanation the test to determine if certain changes are valid.

The proofs used in the examples will be selected from various sources — — plane geometry, calculus, the ordered real numbers. The formal proofs will be in the system of ordered real numbers; and the postulates, definitions, and a selected number of theorems from the system are listed in an appendix.

2·A The Contrapositive and *Reductio ad Absurdum*

There are special terms assigned to statements that are related to an implication.

Definition 5: For the implication $p \Rightarrow q$, the following associated implications are named as indicated:

$$q \Rightarrow p \qquad \text{is the } converse$$

$$\sim p \Rightarrow \sim q \qquad \text{is the } opposite$$

$$\sim q \Rightarrow \sim p \qquad \text{is the } contrapositive$$
$$\text{(opposite converse)}$$

The original implication is logically equivalent to one of its associated forms, and there are other relationships that are mistakenly thought to be valid. The most noted misconception is that the truthfulness of an implication is occasionally thought to give the truth-fulness of the converse. For example, some individuals (fortunately not a large number) seem to accept arguments like the following:

> If you are the murderer, you were in the room.
> You were in the room.
> Therefore, you are the murderer.
>
> If a pair of angles are right angles, then they are equal.
> Hence, a pair of equal angles must be right angles.

For these arguments to be correct, acceptance of the implication would have to give acceptance of the converse. This is *not* the case! If it were, $(p \Rightarrow q) \Rightarrow (q \Rightarrow p)$ would have to be a tautology. But, a simple truth table would show that it is synthetic.

Likewise, a few people think that truthfulness of an implication gives truthfulness of the opposite. It does not since $(p \Rightarrow q) \Rightarrow (\sim p \Rightarrow \sim q)$ is synthetic. In the above example, we could not conclude that a non-murderer was not in the room; and we could not conclude that two non-right angles are unequal.

There is one important equivalence between the above forms, and it is the basis for one of the fundamental proof techniques in mathematics. That is, an implication is equivalent to its contrapositive. A simple truth table verifies the following theorem.

Theorem a $(p \Rightarrow q) \equiv (\sim q \Rightarrow \sim p)$

The equivalence in Theorem a is the basis of the contrapositive proof technique. That is, instead of taking the hypothesis as an assumption and then deriving the conclusion; we assume the negation of the conclusion and show that this implies the negation of the hypothesis. The following is an example from plane geometry.

Theorem b   If lines AB, CD, and AC are such that $\angle BAC + \angle DCA = 180°$, then AB does not intersect CD.

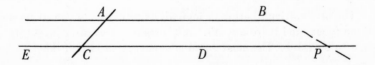

Proof by contrapositive: Assume AB intersects CD at P. Let p be to the right of AC.

Thus, $\angle ECA > \angle BAC$ (exterior angle of a triangle is greater than opposite interior angle);
thus, $\angle ECA + \angle DCA > \angle BAC + \angle DCA$;
but, $\angle ECA + \angle DCA = 180°$;
therefore, $180° > \angle BAC + \angle DCA$.
If P is to the left of AC, a similar proof shows that $180° < \angle BAC + \angle DCA$.

Note that the proof of Theorem b takes the negation of the conclusion as its basic assumption. This assumption leads to a conclusion that $180° > \angle BAC + \angle DCA$ or $180° < \angle BAC + \angle DCA$. Observe that this is the negation of the statement $180° = \angle BAC + \angle DCA$. Thus we have proven in form $\sim q \Rightarrow \sim p$. This is not the same form as the original theorem $p \Rightarrow q$, but Theorem a demonstrates that this is a valid change in the logical form.

When we take the contrapositive of the converse, we observe that we have the opposite. Thus, the converse and the opposite are logically equivalent.

The *implication* $\equiv$ *contrapositive*, and the *converse* $\equiv$ *opposite* equivalences are important to loci proofs in geometry. Suppose we wish to prove that a circle is the locus of points in a plane at a fixed distance from a fixed point. Here we have a locus (the circle) and a condition (a fixed distance from a fixed point). We want to show four things: (i) If a point satisfies the condition, then it is on the locus. (ii) If a point is on the locus, then it satisfies the condition. (iii) If a point is not on the locus, then it does not satisfy the condition, and (iv) If a point does not satisfy the condition, then it is not on the locus. Symbolically these four statements are: (i) $C \Rightarrow L$, (ii) $L \Rightarrow C$, (iii) $\sim L \Rightarrow \sim C$, and (iv) $\sim C \Rightarrow \sim L$. Actually, the last three statements are respectively the converse, contrapositive, and opposite of the first. Thus logical equivalences allow us to prove all four of the statements by a proof of only two. The two that we prove must be carefully selected. For example, we could prove (i) and (ii) to prove the theorem, but a proof that only demonstrated (i) and (iii) would not prove the theorem.

The locus problems in geometry are representative of a general mathematical class of theorems, namely, those theorems that state that some condition is mathematically equivalent to some other condition. These are the "p if and only if q" or "p is a necessary and sufficient condition for q" theorems. Locus problems are in this general type since they say that the condition is satisfied if and only if the point is on the locus.

To prove "p if and only if q" theorems, we should prove the "if" part and the "only if" part. That is, (i) p implies q, and (ii) q implies p. But here we may substitute contrapositives also. The acceptable combinations are:

$$p \Rightarrow q \quad \text{and} \quad q \Rightarrow p$$
$$p \Rightarrow q \quad \text{and} \quad {\sim}p \Rightarrow {\sim}q$$
$${\sim}q \Rightarrow {\sim}p \quad \text{and} \quad q \Rightarrow p$$
$${\sim}q \Rightarrow {\sim}p \quad \text{and} \quad {\sim}p \Rightarrow {\sim}q$$

An unacceptable combination is $p \Rightarrow q$ and ${\sim}q \Rightarrow {\sim}p$.

Example d   In Example b in Chapter 1, a correct proof of the equivalence would be a proof of the following two statements. If triangle ABC is isosceles, then angles BCA and BAC are congruent. If triangle ABC is not isosceles, then angles BCA and BAC are not congruent. An incorrect pair (and thus an incorrect proof) would be the following two: If triangle ABC is isosceles, then angles BCA and BAC are congruent. If angles BAC and BCA are not congruent, then triangle ABC is not isosceles.

In the *reductio ad absurdum* (reduce to the absurd) or *indirect* method of proof, the basic concept is to show that the conclusion must hold by reasoning that it is impossible for it not to hold. That is, we take as a conditional assumption the negation of the conclusion, and we use this along with the hypothesis to derive a contradiction. Instead of proving $p \Rightarrow q$, we prove $(p \wedge {\sim}q) \Rightarrow (r \wedge {\sim}r)$, where r and ${\sim}r$ are the two statements that form the contradiction. The difference between *reductio ad absurdum* and the contrapositive is in the assumptions and derived results. In the *reductio ad absurdum* we have p along with ${\sim}q$ as assumptions, but in the contrapositive we have only ${\sim}q$ as our assumption.

We agree that a theorem may be proved by demonstrating a new theorem that is equivalent in form, in the statement calculus, to the original theorem. Thus, the general correctness of the indirect method of proof is established by the following theorem. The stated equivalence is readily verified with a simple truth table.

Theorem c $(p \Rightarrow q) \equiv ((p \wedge \sim q) \Rightarrow (r \wedge \sim r)$

The term "indirect proof" probably is the result of a situation like the following. We show that $p \Rightarrow q$ must hold by showing that it is impossible for $\sim(p \Rightarrow q)$ to be true. The demonstration that $\sim(p \Rightarrow q)$ is false is accomplished by showing that $\sim(p \Rightarrow q)$ leads to some contradiction, such as $r \wedge \sim r$. But from truth tables we know that $\sim(p \Rightarrow q)$ and $p \wedge \sim q$ are equivalent, so we show $(p \wedge \sim q) \Rightarrow (r \wedge \sim r)$. Observe that this is the form that we discussed above.

Now consider the following example from Euclidean plane geometry.

Theorem d   If coplanar lines AB and CD do not intersect, then then $\angle ABC = \angle DCB$.

Proof by indirect method:

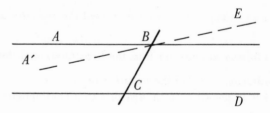

Assume as the hypothesis that AB and CD do not intersect, and assume as the conditional assumption that $\angle ABC \neq \angle DCB$.

One of the two angles is greater than the other, so let $\angle ABC > \angle DCB$.

Construct $\angle CBA'$ interior to $\angle ABC$ such that $\angle CBA' = \angle DCB$.

Let E be a point on $A'B$ such that B is between A' and E.

Thus $\angle EBC + \angle DCB = 180°$. Note theorem b.

61

Hence we have two lines, AB and $A'B$, both parallel to CD through point B.

This contradicts the parallel postulate, namely, that through a point outside of a line, there exists only one parallel to the line.

So we observe that it is impossible for our conditional assumption to hold.

Thus $\angle ABC = \angle DCB$.

It is important to note the difference between this proof and a proof by the contrapositive. The main points in the *reductio ad absurdum* are (i) the use of the hypothesis and the negation of the conclusion as the assumptions, and (ii) the contradiction that is the end result. The contradiction may be any two statements that are incompatible. Whereas in the contrapositive, the negation of the original conclusion is our only assumption, and the negation of the original hypothesis is the statement that we derive.

EXERCISES (§ 2·A)

1. Find an example of a proof that used the *reductio ad absurdum* and:

(a) the contradiction is different from the hypothesis and the conclusion.

(b) the contradiction is p and the negation of p.
(Decide if it is possible to change this to a contrapositive.)

(c) the contradiction is q and the negation of q.
(Decide if it is possible to change this to a direct proof.)

2. Construct tautologies that justify the techniques in Exercise 1 (b) and (c).

3. Find the converse, opposite, and the contrapositive of the following:

(a) $\sim p \Rightarrow q$

(b) $\sim p \Rightarrow \sim q$

(c) $q \Rightarrow \sim p$

(d) $p \Rightarrow (q \Rightarrow r)$

(e) If it rains, the grass is wet.

(f) If a number is rational, then it is expressible as the quotient of two integers.

(g) A necessary condition for series convergence is that the nth term go to zero.

(h) A sufficient condition that two lines are parallel is that they are perpendicular to the same line.

4. List the possible pairs of (i) $C \Rightarrow L$, (ii) $L \Rightarrow C$, (iii) $\sim L \Rightarrow \sim C$, and (iv) $\sim C \Rightarrow \sim L$ that prove a locus theorem. List the pairs that do not.

5. Why is the contrapositive also called the opposite converse?

6. Examine the following theorems and proofs. Then explain the logic techniques employed.

(a) *Theorem:* The positive integer a is even if and only if a^2 is even.

Proof: If a is not even then a can be expressed as $2n+1$. Thus, $a^2 = (2n+1)^2 = 4n^2 + 4n + 1 = 2(2n^2 + 2n) + 1 = 2k+1$, and a^2 is not even. Whenever a is even, a may be expressed as $2n$. Thus, $a^2 = 4n^2 = 2(2n^2) = 2k$ and a^2 is even.

(b) *Theorem:* If the sequence of positive integers $\{a_k\}$, $k = 1, 2, \ldots$ is unbounded, then the subsequence $\{a_k\}$, $k = j, j+1 \ldots$ is unbounded for any fixed integer j.

Proof: Assume that M is an upper bound for $\{a_k\}$, $k = j, j + 1, \ldots$. That is $a_k \leq M$ for any $k \geq j$. The finite set $a_1, a_2, \ldots, a_{j-1}$ has a largest member, say L. Therefore, $a_k \leq L + M$ for $k \geq 1$, and we see that the sequence $\{a_k\}$, $k = 1, 2, \ldots$ is bounded.

7. The following theorems are from plane geometry. State the assumptions that would be made in a *reductio ad absurdum* proof. Then state the assumption that would be made in a contrapositive proof. What could be the respective conclusions?

Theorem: If two internal angle bisectors are equal, then the triangle is isosceles.

Theorem: If two medians of the triangle are equal, then the triangle is isosceles.

8. Explain why some authors call $p \Rightarrow (r \Rightarrow q)$ "the converse" of $p \Rightarrow (q \Rightarrow r)$. Would "a converse" be better? Would it be correct? Would "a type of converse" be better still? Would it be correct?

9. In the proof of a theorem of the form $p \Longleftrightarrow (q \lor r)$:

(a) What is the conclusion for a proof of the "if" part with a contrapositive technique?

(b) What is the hypothesis for a proof of the "only if" part with a *reductio ad absurdum* technique?

2·B   Operators in the hypothesis or conclusion

The contrapositive and *reductio ad absurdum* are standard proof changes, but there are other techniques that are nonstandard. Sometimes these techniques may be very subtle. We initiate their investigation with a very elementary one — — conjunction changes. That is, what are the techniques used when a conjunction appears in the hypothesis, $(p \land q) \Rightarrow r$, or in the conclusion, $p \Rightarrow (q \land r)$? Conjunction changes are somewhat trivial, but the elementary discussion here leads readily into the more complicated material.

In general a change in the logical form is considered to be valid when either (i) the stated form and the substituted form are logically equivalent, or (ii) the substituted form "implies" the original form. In the first situation, the usual one, it is obvious that a statement form may be replaced by its logical equivalent. For example, in the contrapositive technique an equivalent form, $\sim q \Rightarrow \sim p$, is proved instead of the original form, $p \Rightarrow q$. In situation (ii), the individual may find it convenient to substitute a stronger form. That is, a form that is not equivalent but that implies the original form. A formula, ϕ, is said to *imply* a formula, ψ, when $\phi \Rightarrow \psi$ is a tautology. For example, in the following comments on conjunction, we will find it convenient in Example e to prove $p \Rightarrow r$ instead of the stated form $(p \land q) \Rightarrow r$. This is a valid change since

$(p \Rightarrow r) \Rightarrow ((p \wedge q) \Rightarrow r)$ is a tautology. Note that in this case we actually prove a theorem that is stronger than the one requested. This odd state of affairs, doing more than what is necessary, is unusual; but there are occasions when it is convenient.

If the conjunction is in the conclusion, that is, $p \Rightarrow (q \wedge r)$, then we must prove both q and r as consequences of the hypothesis, p. Generally this is accomplished with two different proofs, namely, $p \Rightarrow q$ and $p \Rightarrow r$. The following theorem demonstrates that this substitution is valid; the simple truth table proof is omitted.

Theorem e $(p \Rightarrow (q \wedge r)) \equiv ((p \Rightarrow q) \wedge (p \Rightarrow r))$

Example e   If $a > 0$, then $a^2 > 0$ and $|a| = a$

Proof: Assume $a > 0$

Thus we have $a > 0$ and $a > 0$, and $a \cdot a = a^2$.
Now $O\,4$ gives $a^2 > 0$.
Now if $a > 0$, the definition of absolute value, $D\,4$, gives $|a| = a.$*

Note that the proof is actually the proof of two theorems: $(a > 0) \Rightarrow (a^2 > 0)$ and $(a > 0) \Rightarrow (|a| = a)$.

If the conjunction is in the hypothesis, $(p \wedge q) \Rightarrow r$, then our assumptions are the statement p and the statement q. Usually no substitution is required, but occasionally one of the assumptions is not needed and the author might prove $p \Rightarrow r$ instead. This is a somewhat unusual change, but it is valid.

Theorem f $(p \Rightarrow r) \Rightarrow ((p \wedge q) \Rightarrow r)$

Example f   If $a > 0$ and $b > 0$, then $a^2 > 0$.

Proof: Assume $a > 0$, then $a \cdot a = a^2$ and $a^2 > 0$ by $O\,4$.

Note that we did not use the $b > 0$ hypothesis. The statement, "You do not have to use an hypothesis if you do not need it," is applicable here. But a warning should be noted; "A careful author does not make a practice of putting in superfluous hypotheses, so when you fail to use all the given information there is some possibility that your proof is in error."

---

* See appendix for Definition $D4$ and postulate $O4$.

The conjunction in the hypothesis and conclusion is most likely to occur when you need to apply a definition and the definition is given as a conjunction of conditions. For example, in the study of relations, an equivalence relation is defined as one that is reflexive, symmetric, and transitive. Thus an hypothesis involving an equivalence relation would in fact assume three properties, and the student could employ any or all of the three. Likewise a conclusion that required an equivalence relation would call for a proof of all three conditions — — reflexivity, symmetry, and transitivity.

The logical substitutions in regard to an implication in the conclusion are generally hidden in the subtle wording of the proof. That is, when a theorem is stated as $p \Rightarrow (q \Rightarrow r)$, the author usually proves $(p \wedge q) \Rightarrow r$ and fails to mention that he has changed the form. The following theorem demonstrates that the change is valid.

Theorem g $(p \Rightarrow (q \Rightarrow r)) \equiv ((p \wedge q) \Rightarrow r)$

Also the author might find it convenient to use a contrapositive substitution along with the proof technique outlined in Theorem g. This logical substitution is justified by the following theorem.

Theorem h $(p \Rightarrow (q \Rightarrow r)) \equiv ((p \wedge \sim r) \Rightarrow \sim q)$

Example g If $a < d$, then $b < c$ is a sufficient condition for $a + b < c + d$.

Formal proof:
$$\text{assume } a < d \text{ and } b < c$$

$a + b < d + b$	O3*
$b + d < c + d$	O3
$b + d = d + b$	A5
$a + b < b + d$	substitution of equals
$a + b < c + d$	O2

Informal alternate proof:
Assume $a < d$ and $a + b \geq c + d$.
Thus $a + b - c - d \geq 0$ and $d - a > 0$.
Hence $a + b - c - d + d - a \geq 0$,
or $b - c \geq 0$ and $b \geq c$.

---

* See appendix.

Note that $a + b \geq c + d$ is the negation of $a + b < c + d$ and $b \geq c$ is the negation of $b < c$.

When a biconditional is present in the conclusion, we have a combination of the implication and conjunction techniques. The form of the theorem is usually $p \Rightarrow (q \Leftrightarrow r)$ and the authors generally prove instead $(p \wedge q) \Rightarrow r$ and $(p \wedge r) \Rightarrow q$. This is a valid substitution as seen by the following theorem.

Theorem i
$$(p \Rightarrow (q \Leftrightarrow r)) \equiv (((p \wedge q) \Rightarrow r) \wedge ((p \wedge r) \Rightarrow q))$$

This situation generally happens when you have an equivalence under a particular hypothesis. For example, "In positive numbers, the order of the squares is equivalent to the order of the numbers", "In absolute geometry, the parallel postulate is equivalent to the existence of similar triangles", and "In a Hilbert space; the following conditions are equivalent, (a) the space is separable, (b) the space has a countable orthonormal basis."

Theorem j When $a, b > 0$; $a > b$ is a necessary and sufficient condition for $a^2 > b^2$.

First proof:
  "*sufficiency*": Assume $a, b > 0$ and $a > b$.

$a + b > b$	$O\,3$
$a + b > 0$	$O\,2$
$a + {}^{-}b > b + {}^{-}b$	$O\,3$
$b + {}^{-}b = 0$	$A\,4$
$a + {}^{-}b > 0$	$O\,2$
$(a + {}^{-}b)(a + b) > 0$	$O\,4$
$a^2 + {}^{-}b^2 > 0$	$T\,2$
$a^2 + {}^{-}b^2 + b^2 > b^2$	$O\,3$
$a^2 > b^2$	$A\,4$

  "*necessity*": Assume $a, b > 0$ and $a^2 > b^2$.
  Thus $(a + b) > 0$ and $a^2 + {}^{-}b^2 > 0$.
  Therefore $(a^2 + {}^{-}b^2)(a + b)^{-1} > 0$ and $a + {}^{-}b > 0$.
  So $a > b$.

Informal alternate proof:
  Since a, b and $a - b$ are all positive, we see that $a^2 >$

$ab > b^2$ holds. Now if a and b are positive and $b - a$ is non-negative, we see that $b^2 - a^2$ is non-negative.

The difficult point here is that some authors do not indicate the division between the sufficiency and necessity, as the alternate proof illustrates. Needless to say this does not help the student in his attempts at understanding.

Now we assume that we have a theorem to prove with an implication as its hypothesis, that is, $(p \Rightarrow q) \Rightarrow r$. The implication in the hypothesis, $p \Rightarrow q$, states only the relationship between p and q. We know that q happens whenever p happens, but we do not know the specific truth values of either p or q. That is, p may be true or false and q may be true or false, and we know only that the truthfulness of p ensures the truthfulness of q. In other words, the truth value of q is conditioned by the truth value of p. This situation occurs frequently within the body of a proof, but we will treat it as a full theorem. The logic techniques are the same and the reader may either apply these techniques to a full theorem or to a subtheorem within the body of a proof.

A *reductio ad absurdum* approach is convenient to use in the implication in the hypothesis situation. This approach furnishes as "given" information the original hypothesis, $p \Rightarrow q$, and the negation of the original conclusion, $\sim r$. Then a proof that leads to a contradiction is desired. The equivalence of the statement forms gives the following theorem.

Theorem k
$$((p \Rightarrow q) \Rightarrow r) \equiv (((p \Rightarrow q) \wedge \sim r) \Rightarrow (s \wedge \sim s))$$

Example h   If $a + b \leq c$ whenever $b < 0$, then $a \leq c$.

> *Proof:* Assume $b < 0$ implies $a + b \leq c$, and $a > c$.
> Hence $c - a < 0$ and $(c - a)/2 < 0$.
> If we let $(c - a)/2$ play the role of b in the implication, then we have $a + (c - a)/2 \leq c$.
> Consequently $(a + c)/2 \leq c$, $a + c \leq 2c$, and $a \leq c$.
> But, $a \leq c$ and $a > c$ are contradictory and the proof is complete.

Notice that the preceding example is an instance of a peculiar form of the *reductio ad absurdum*. That is, the contradiction is our conditional assumption, $\sim r$, and the original conclusion, r. The statement form equivalence employed here is

$$((p \Rightarrow q) \Rightarrow r) \equiv (((p \Rightarrow q) \wedge \sim r) \Rightarrow (r \wedge \sim r)).$$

Consequently the substitution is valid and the proof is correct.

With an implication in the hypothesis, $(p \Rightarrow q) \Rightarrow r$, the reader may occasionally use a contrapositive substitution. This gives $\sim r \Rightarrow \sim (p \Rightarrow q)$. So we have $\sim r$ as our "given", and the negation of p implies q as our "to prove." Remember that an implication is false only when the hypothesis is true and the conclusion is false. So we might suspect that the negation of an implication would be a conjunction of the antecedent and the negation of the consequence. This analysis is correct as seen by the equivalence $\sim (p \Rightarrow q) \equiv (p \wedge \sim q)$. Thus we have another technique for proofs that involves an implication in the hypothesis.

Theorem I $((p \Rightarrow q) \Rightarrow r) \equiv (\sim r \Rightarrow (p \wedge \sim q))$

Example i   The condition $a \leq 1$ is necessary for $a \geq 1$ to imply that $a = 1$.

Proof: Assume $a > 1$.
          Consequently $a \geq 1$ and $a \neq 1$.

The above example could have as its statement $(a \geq 1 \Rightarrow a = 1) \Rightarrow a \leq 1$. In the proof we take as our assumption $a > 1$, that is, not $(a \leq 1)$; and then we derive $a \geq 1$ and $a \neq 1$. The substitution employed here is the equivalence stated in Theroem 1.

In case the theorem has a couple of implications in the hypothesis and an implication in the conclusion, then a direct proof is generally best.

Example j   A sufficient condition that the ΔABC be isosceles is that ΔABC have equal interior angle bisectors. A necessary condition that ΔABC be isosceles is that ΔABC have equal medians. Therefore, ΔABC has equal medians whenever it has equal interior angle bisectors.

The assumptions: (i) If ΔABC has equal interior angle bisectors, then it is isosceles, (ii) If ΔABC is isosceles, then it has equal medians, and (iii) The $\triangle ABC$ has equal interior angle bisectors; these assumptions readily give the conclusion — — the $\triangle ABC$ has equal medians. Here the substitution is

$$((p \Rightarrow q) \wedge (r \Rightarrow s) \wedge t) \Rightarrow u \text{ for}$$
$$((p \Rightarrow q) \wedge (r \Rightarrow s)) \Rightarrow (t \Rightarrow u).$$

Note that the technique illustrated in Example j is the general concept of a proof. That is, a theorem is usually stated as $p \Rightarrow q$ and the proof arrives at q, under the hypothesis p, by a sequence of implication steps. First we prove $p \Rightarrow s_1$, then $s_1 \Rightarrow s_2$, $s_2 \Rightarrow s_3$, $\ldots$, $s_{n-1} \Rightarrow s_n$, and $s_n \Rightarrow q$. The assertion that this gives the theorem is of course an application of the elementary relationship:

$$((p \Rightarrow s_1) \wedge (s_1 \Rightarrow s_2) \wedge \ldots \wedge (s_n \Rightarrow q)) \Rightarrow (p \Rightarrow q).$$

An "or" connective within the structure of a theorem occasionally generates confusion in the interpretation. The reason is that a disjunction of two statements does not imply that either of the statements is known to be true. A true disjunction simply says that not both of the statements are false. Generally it is more convenient to use a contrapositive argument and work with a more definite form of interpretation. That is, a form in which a concrete statement is assumed and particular statements are to be proved. So, in the event of a disjunction in the hypothesis, the contrapositive may be taken and a DeMorgan Law applied. This results in the following equivalence: $((p \vee q) \Rightarrow r) \equiv (\sim r \Rightarrow (\sim p \wedge \sim q))$. The same attack, contrapositive with a DeMorgan Law, generates a technique for working with a disjunction in the conclusion: $(p \Rightarrow (q \vee r)) \equiv ((\sim q \wedge \sim r) \Rightarrow \sim p)$.

Occasionally a theorem will have disjunctions in both the hypothesis and the conclusion. Then a combination of the techniques or a new variation might be employed. It is also important to note that the "or" connective might be hidden in the mathematical notation. For example, an unapparent "or" connective is present in the symbol "$\leq$."

Example k   If $ab \leq 0$, then $a \geq 0$ or $b \geq 0$.

Proof: Assume $a < 0$ and $b < 0$.
Therefore, $T5$ gives $ab > 0$.*

---

* See Appendix for $T5$ and all subsequent combinations of a letter and number.

In fact, Example k has a collection of four "or" connectives, but the proof technique primarily employs a change in one of them — —the main connective in the conclusion. The other "or" connectives, in the symbol $\leq$, are dispensed with in the observation that "not $(ab \leq 0)$" must be "$ab > 0$". In a similar manner "not $(a \geq 0)$" and "not $(b \geq 0)$" must be "$a < 0$" and "$b < 0$" respectively. At first we might have doubts that the proof in example k actually proves the theorem. The proof is in fact the theorem "If $a < 0$ and $b < 0$, then $ab > 0$." But this change is valid when we see that it is in the form $(\sim q \wedge \sim r)$ $\Rightarrow \sim p$ and the theorem is in the equivalent form $p \Rightarrow (q \vee r)$.

We now illustrate another technique that might be used for disjunction in the conclusion. In the following example we prove a theorem that is basic to the algebraic technique of equation solving by factoring.

Example l   If $ab = 0$, then $a = 0$ or $b = 0$.

> *Proof:* Assume $ab = 0$ and $a \neq 0$.
> Thus a^{-1} exists by $M4$
> and $a^{-1}(ab) = a^{-1}0 = 0$ by $ME2$ and $T6$.
> But $a^{-1}(ab) = (a^{-1}a)b = 1b = b$
> and we see that $b = 0$.

Note that the form of the theorem is $p \Rightarrow (q \vee r)$ and we have proved $(p \wedge \sim q) \Rightarrow r$. The question is: Is this a valid substitution? The answer is seen to be affirmative when the following equivalence is observed. A common error is that some students feel than an additional proof of $(p \wedge \sim r) \Rightarrow q$ is needed here.

Theorem m $(p \Rightarrow (q \vee r)) \equiv ((p \wedge \sim q) \Rightarrow r)$

Remember that in mathematics "or" is interpreted in the inclusive sense unless the author specifically indicated the exclusive sense. The following example includes an exclusive disjunction and it illustrates a logic technique that is applicable.

Example m   If $ab < 0$, then exactly one of the numbers a or b is negative.

> *Proof:* Assume $ab < 0$, and a is non-negative.
> That is $a > 0$ or $a = 0$.

If $a > 0$, then $M4$ and $T3$ state that a^{-1} exists and $a^{-1} > 0$.

Thus, by $M4$, $T1$, and $O4$ we have $a^{-1}(ab) < 0$ and $a^{-1}(ab) = (a^{-1}a)b = 1b = b$.

So we have $b < 0$.

Now if $a = 0$, we have by $T6$, $ab = 0$.

But if $a < 0$ and $b < 0$, then $T5$ gives $ab > 0$.

Hence ab is non-negative.

Note that the theorem has as its statement form $p \Rightarrow (q \lor r)$, and the statement form of the proof is $((p \land \sim q) \Rightarrow r) \land ((q \land r) \Rightarrow \sim p)$. This equivalence is stated as Theorem n. The reader might observe that there are many substitutions within the body of the proof. First of all, in the proof of "If $ab > 0$ and $a \geq 0$, then $b < 0$."; the proof is broken into two parts. (i) If $ab < 0$ and $a > 0$, then $b < 0$. (ii) not $(ab < 0$ and $a = 0)$. So with the notation that $\sim q$ is $(s \lor t)$ with s representing $a > 0$ and t representing $a = 0$, we see that the valid substitution is $((p \land s) \Rightarrow r) \land \sim(p \land t)$ replacing $(p \land \sim(s \lor t)) \Rightarrow r$. The reader may verify that the proper equivalence does exist. Next, in the final conclusion of $ab \geq 0$, a simple remark "if $ab > 0$, then $ab > 0$ or $ab = 0$" is used. Obviously this is a valid assertion, that is, $u \Rightarrow u \lor w$.

Theorem n $(p \Rightarrow (q \lor r)) \equiv ((p \land \sim q) \Rightarrow r) \land ((q \land r) \Rightarrow \sim p)$

The partitioning of the proof in Example m leads us into the relationship between disjunction and proof by case investigations. Many times it is possible to prove a theorem by considering the various cases, and this type of proof employs various equivalent statement forms. Needless to say, in any proof that involves cases; it is extremely important to make sure that every possible case has been investigated.

Our examples of case proofs are taken from plane Euclidean geometry and the theory of absolute values.

Example n In a triangle ABC, if angle A is larger than angle B, then the side opposite angle A is larger than the side opposite angle B.

Proof: Let a and b represent the length of the sides respectively opposite angles A and B.

Case 1. If $a = b$, then we know that triangle ABC is isosceles and angles A and B are equal.

Case 2. If $a < b$ then construct a point D on AC in such a way that CD is equal to length a. Now triangle CDB is seen to be isosceles. Thus angles CBD and CDB are equal. But, angle B is larger than angle CBD and angle CDB is larger than angle A. Thus angle B is larger than angle A.

Here the proof is by a contrapositive technique. Namely, $a \leq b$ implies angle $A \leq$ angle B. So what we want to prove has as its statement form $(p \lor q) \Rightarrow (r \lor s)$ and we proved $p \Rightarrow r$ and $q \Rightarrow s$. So in effect our substitution is the valid one of $(p \Rightarrow r) \land (q \Rightarrow s)$ for $(p \lor q) \Rightarrow (r \lor s)$.

Example o $|a^2| = a^2$

Proof:

Case 1. If $a > 0$, then $O4$ gives $a^2 > 0$.
So $|a^2| = a^2$ by $D4$

Case 2. If $a = 0$, then $T6$ gives $a^2 = 0$.
So $|a^2| = |0| = 0$ by $D4$

Case 3. If $a < 0$, then $T5$ gives $a^2 > 0$.
So $|a^2| = a^2$ by $D4$.

Therefore $|a^2| = a^2$

Observe that we actually prove $(a > 0$ or $a = 0$ or $a < 0)$ implies $|a^2| = a^2$. But we know $a > 0$, $a = 0$, or $a < 0$ by $O1$. Thus the basic equivalence is $((p \lor q \lor r) \Rightarrow s) \land (p \lor q \lor r)) \equiv s$, where p, q, r, and s represent $a > 0$, $a = 0$, $a < 0$, and $|a^2| = a^2$, respectively.

Example p The integer $(n^2 + n)$ is even.

Proof:

Case 1. If n is even, then n may be expressed as $2k$. Thus $n^2 + n = (2k)^2 + 2k = 4k^2 + 2k = 2(2k^2 + k) = 2j$.

Case 2. If n is odd, then n may be expressed as $2i + 1$.
Thus $n^2 + n = (2i + 1)^2 + 2(i + 1) = 4i^2 + 4i + 1 + 2i + 1 = 2(2i^2 + 3i + 1) = 2m$.

Here the example illustrates a typical mathematical technique. That is, when you want to demonstrate q, then demonstrate $p \Rightarrow q$ and $\sim p \Rightarrow q$ and employ the equivalence $((p \Rightarrow q) \wedge (\sim p \Rightarrow q)) \equiv q$.

EXERCISES (§ 2 · B)

1. (a) Prove: If $a < 0$ and $b > 0$, then $ab < 0$ and $a/b < 0$.

   (b) Outline the logical changes and explain their validity.

2. Fill in the missing details in the formal proof of the "necessity" part of Theorem j.

3. Explain the informal proof of Theorem j.

4. If $a > 0$, then $ab > 0$ if and only if $b > 0$.

(a) Give an informal proof of the above theorem.

(b) Give a formal proof of the above theorem.

5. If $a^2 > b^2$, then (i) $a > 0$ is a sufficient condition that $a > b$. (ii) $a < b$ is a necessary condition that $a < 0$.

(a) Give an informal proof of the above theorem.

(b) Give a formal proof of the above theorem.

6. Prove (a) formally and (b) informally:
If $a > b$, then $ac > bc$ if $c > 0$ and $ac < bc$ if $c < 0$.

7. Explain why Theorem j is the basic idea that is used whenever you square both sides of an inequality, or find their square roots.

8. Try to prove Example h with a contrapositive substitution. Note that this is an instance of a *reductio ad absurdum* proof that does not readily allow a contrapositive technique.

9. Prove: If $a < b + c$ whenever $c > 0$, then $a \leqq b$.

Hint: Note Example h.

10. Prove: If $a < 0$ whenever $a \leq 0$, then $a \neq 0$.

11. Prove: If $b < c$ whenever $c \geq 0$, then $b < 0$.

12. Show that $((p \Rightarrow q) \wedge {\sim}r) \Rightarrow r$ is a valid substitution for $(p \Rightarrow q) \Rightarrow r$. Find or construct an example of a proof that uses this technique.

13. Prove: If $b \leq c$ whenever $c \leq 0$, then $0 < c$ whenever $b > c$.

14. Look up the concepts of reflexive, symmetric, and transitive relations. Then investigate the following incorrect theorem and proof.

Theorem (sic): A symmetric and transitive relation must be reflexive.

Proof (sic): Since the relation is symmetric, a related to b gives b related to a. Thus a related to b and b related to a gives, by transitivity, that a is related to a.

15. Prove by cases: If $a \geq 0$ and $b \geq 0$, then $ab \geq 0$.

16. Explain why an additional proof of "If $ab = 0$ and $b \neq 0$, then $a \neq 0$" is not needed in Example l.

17. Explain why $((p \wedge q) \Rightarrow r) \wedge (({\sim}q \wedge {\sim}r) \Rightarrow {\sim}p)$ would not be a correct substitution to use in Example l. This is a very common erroneous substitution.

18. Prove by cases: $|ab| = |a|\,|b|$. Outline the related logic.

19. Prove by cases: If $a \neq 0$, then $a^2 > 0$.
Outline the related logic.

20. Prove by cases: $|a + b| \leq |a| + |b|$.
Outline the related logic.

21. Prove by cases: $|a| - |b| \leq |a - b|$.
Outline the related logic.

22. Prove: If it is not the case that $a > 0$ or $b > 0$, then $ab \geq 0$.

23. Analyze the following "theorems" and "proofs."

(a) "*Theorem*": $a^2 - 2a + 1 = 0$ if and only if $a = 1$.

    "*Proof*": If $a = 1$, $a^2 - 2a + 1 = 1 - 2 + 1 = 0$. If $a^2 - 2a + 1 = 0$, $(a - 1)^2 = 0$, $a - 1 = 0$ and so $a = 1$.

(b) "*Theorem*": The product of positive integers m and n is odd if and only if m is odd and n is odd.

    "*Proof*": If m is odd and n is odd, $m = 2k + 1$ and $n = 2j + 1$, $mn = (2k + 1)(2j + 1) = 2(2kj + k + j) + 1$ and so mn is odd. If mn is even then $mn = 2i$ and so m or n has a 2 factor and thus either m is even or n is even.

(c) "*Theorem*": If $ab \geq 0$; then either $a \geq 0$ and $b \geq 0$, or $a \leq 0$ and $b \leq 0$.

    "*Proof*": If $ab \geq 0$ and either $a > 0$ or $b > 0$, then either $\frac{1}{a}(ab) \geq 0 \cdot \frac{1}{a}$ or $\frac{1}{b}(ab) \geq 0\frac{1}{b}$ and so either $a > 0$ and $b \geq 0$ or $b > 0$ and $a \geq 0$ and so $a \geq 0$ and $b \geq 0$.

(d) "*Theorem*": If a and b are real numbers, then $a^2 + b^2 = 0$ if and only if $a = 0$ and $b = 0$.

    "*Proof*": If a and b are real numbers and $a = 0$ and $b = 0$, then $a^2 + b^2 = 0 + 0 = 0$. If a and b are real numbers and either $a \neq 0$ or $b \neq 0$, then $a^2 > 0$ or $b^2 > 0$ and so $a^2 + b^2 > 0$ and thus $a^2 + b^2 \neq 0$.

(e) "*Theorem*": If either $a < b$ and $a > -b$, or $a > b$ and $a < -b$, then $a^2 < b^2$.

    "*Proof*": If $a^2 \geq b^2$, then $a^2 - b^2 \geq 0$, $(a - b)(a + b) \geq 0$ and so either $a - b \geq 0$ and $a + b \geq 0$, or $a - b \leq 0$ and $a + b \leq 0$. Thus either $a \geq b$ and $a \geq -b$, or $a \leq b$ and $a \leq -b$.

24. Symbolize the following theorem as given by Cairns.*

"Theorem 1. The linear graph G is unicursal if and only if it is connected and either (1) there are no odd vertices, in which case the initial and terminal points of a unicursal tracing must coincide but can otherwise be arbitrarily selected; or (2) there are exactly two odd vertices, in which case the unicursal tracing must start at one odd vertex (either will do) and terminate at the other."

* Stewart S. Cairns, *Introductory Topology* (New York: The Ronald Press Co., © 1961) p. 5.

II

THE FUNCTION CALCULUS

Chapter 5

THE FUNCTION CALCULUS
OF ONE VARIABLE

We now proceed to the investigation of open sentences and quantifiers. An open sentence is an expression that involves either a pronoun or a mathematical variable, and we established in Part I that they do not have truth value until their undetermined entities are specified or restricted. For example, "He is over six feet tall" is neither true nor false until he is specified; and "$x^2 - 1 = (x + 1)(x - 1)$" has its truth value dependent on the restriction placed on the variable x. We now will formalize the techniques for analysis of arguments that involve these open expressions and their related quantification. This analysis must consider the predicate structures, along with the truth value as a function of the variable values. Consequently we term these investigations "the function calculus."

> **Definition 1:** An *open sentence* is a declarative sentence that contains one or more variables in such a manner that a replacement of each variable by specific symbols from a designated set establishes the sentence as a statement.

§1 STATEMENT FUNCTIONS AND QUANTIFIERS

In general an open sentence involves a variable and a predicate relationship. We refer to the variables as individual variables and we symbolize them with letters from the end of the alphabet and possibly with subscripts: x, y, z, x_1, x_2, etc. We symbolize the predicate concepts either with capital letters that suggest the verb present or with the capital letters P, Q, R. For example, "He is over six feet tall" would be symbolized as $S(x)$. Here S indicates the relationship "is over six feet tall" and x is the individual variable that symbolizes the general individual he. The expression $S(x)$ is verbalized as "S of x" and it means that the individual variable x is associated with the predicate relationship S in such a manner that a substitution of a specific value from a designated set for the individual variable x will establish the sentence as a statement. In cases where no confusion is present, we will shorten the notation, as Sx.

The reader should note an immediate resemblance between our statement function $S(x)$ and the usual expression for a mathematical function $f(x)$. This resemblance is intentional since a value of the function and a statement given by the statement function are both generated by particular substituted values.

> **Definition 2:** A *statement function* of one individual variable is a collection of symbols that represent an open sentence of one variable, for example, $P(x)$ where P represents the predicate relationship of the sentence and x represents the individual variable.

In mathematics, a solution set to $f(x) = a$ is the set of values of the variable present in the domain of the function that satisfy the relationship $f(x) = a$, and in an analogous manner the instances of the individual variables that give $\tau(P(x)) = T$ is called the *truth set* of the statement function $P(x)$. The *domain of discussion* is the set of values of the individual variable that are meaningful when substituted into the statement function, that is, the collection of values of the individual variable that are such that substitution of them into the statement function yields a statement. The domain of discussion is occasionally called the *universe*. Thus the truth set will be contained in the domain of discussion and its members will be the particular instances of the individual variable that give under substitution a true statement.

For example, consider the open sentence "He is over six feet tall" and its related statement function $S(x)$. The domain of discussion would generally be selected as the class of all males. One member is Lyndon B. Johnson and substitution of this particular value of the variable gives the true statement −− Lyndon B. Johnson is over six feet tall. Thus Lyndon B. Johnson is an element of the truth set of this statement function.

In the mathematical example $x^2 = 1$, symbolized as $P(x)$, the domain of discussion must be specified. First of all consider the domain as the set of positive integers. Then the truth set would be the set that has the single element 1. If the domain is specified as the set of real numbers, then the truth set consists of 1 and −1. Observe that the truth set of a mathematical open sentence is often the familiar solution set.

The analysis of statement functions has a basic dependence on the domain of discussion. Usually this domain is tacitly understood to be a particular set, but if there is any confusion or ambiguity present the author should specify the intended domain, in other words, the universe. To examine these ideas, consider a particular domain consisting of the integers between zero and three inclusive, i.e., $\mathfrak{D} = \{0, 1, 2, 3\}$. The symbol $\mathfrak{D}$, "script D," will be used exclusively for "domain." We could state many open sentences related to this domain, but consider the following in particular:

(i) x is non-negative.

(ii) x is even.

If we establish the symbols E and N for the respective predicate relationships "is even" and "is non-negative," then we can symbolize the open sentences in the following manner:

(i) $N(x)$

(ii) $E(x)$

Both of the statement functions have particular truth sets, but $N(x)$ is unique in that its truth set is the complete domain. In case a propositional function has its truth set identical with its domain we can convert the open sentence to a true statement by the addition of an assertion to this effect. That is, "For all integers x between zero and three inclusive, x is non-negative"; or in case the domain of discussion is understood −− "For all x, x is non-negative". This is the universal quantifier and it is symbolized as $\forall\, x \,\epsilon\, \mathfrak{D}$ or $\forall\, x$ in case the domain is understood.* The notation is sometimes shortened to simply (x), but we will refrain from this since the symbol can be confused with an occurrence of x that is not intended to be a quantifier.

Definition 3: The *universal quantifier* is the symbol, $\forall\, x$, that specifies complete assertion for the domain of discussion.

---

* ϵ is the membership symbol from set theory. It is verbalized as "element of".

The truth value of a universally quantified statement function is given by:

$\tau((\forall x \ \epsilon \ \mathcal{D}) \ P(X)) = $ T if and only if a true statement is given by every replacement of the individual variable by individual members of the domain into the open sentence symbolized as $P(x)$.

The universal quantifier is verbalized as "all x" and it is the translation of the following language expressions: "For all x," "For every x," "For each x," "All things x," "Everything x," and "Each thing x."

The prefacing of $E(x)$ in the above example with a universal quantifier would convert the open sentence to a statement, but it would have truth value F. There is of course a conversion of the open sentence to a true statement, but the prefix clause would have to assert the existence of a particular x. This would be the existential quantifier. That is, "There exists an integer x between zero and three inclusive such that x is even." The existential quantifier is symbolized as $\exists \ x \ \epsilon \ \mathcal{D}$ or briefly $\exists x$ whenever the domain is understood. The symbol is verbalized as "there exists an x" and it is the translation of the following language expressions: "For some x," "Some x is," "There exists an x," "There is an x," and "There is at least one x." The expressions "Many x" and "exactly one x" suggest additional meanings, and the symbol $\exists!$ is usually used for "exactly one x." We are not interested in so complicated an analysis, so we will translate both expressions ("many x" and "exactly one x") as "there exists an x."

Definition 4: The *existential quantifier* is the symbol, $\exists x$, that specifies assertion for some elements of the domain. The truth value of an existentially quantified statement function is given by:

$\tau((\exists x \ \epsilon \ \mathcal{D}) \ P(x)) = $ T if and only there is at least one member of the domain that is such that a true statement is generated when this member is substituted for the individual variable in the symbolized open sentence $P(x)$.

The statement formula, $E(x)$, given above will give a true statement when prefixed with an existential quantifier, that is, $\tau((\exists x \ \epsilon \ \mathcal{D}) \ E(x)) = $T. Likewise $\tau((\exists x \ \epsilon \ \mathcal{D}) \ N(x)) = $ T. This is a hint of one of the first theorems that we will give in a later section —— If the domain is non-empty, then $((\mathrm{V}\, x\, \epsilon\, \mathfrak{D})\, P(x)) \implies ((\exists\, x\, \epsilon\, \mathfrak{D})\, P(x))$. This result is immediate by the following considerations: If there are things in the domain and all things in the domain satisfy the predicate relationship $P(x)$, then there are things that satisfy the predicate relationship $P(x)$.

It is interesting to note that the universal and existential quantifier are somewhat generalized conjunctions and disjunctions. That is, in regard to the earlier example concerned with the domain of integers between zero and three inclusive, we could express the following:

$$((\mathrm{V}\, x\, \epsilon\, \mathfrak{D})\, N(x)) \equiv (N(0) \wedge (N(1) \wedge (N(2) \wedge N(3))))$$

$$((\exists\, x\, \epsilon\, \mathfrak{D})\, E(x)) \equiv (E(0) \vee (E(1) \vee (E(2) \vee E(3))))$$

This injects the question "Why have quantifiers?" Of course, quantifiers may be expressed as strings of conjunctions or disjunctions only when the domain is finite. We are interested in many infinite domains, e.g. the real numbers; so the analysis of the function calculus is necessary.

EXERCISES (§ 1.)

1. Use the indicated predicate variables and domains to symbolize the following as quantified statement functions. Specify the truth value of each statement formed.

(a) All freshmen study. $\mathfrak{D}$: college freshmen S: study

(b) Some freshmen study.

(c) Some cows have horns. $\mathfrak{D}$: American cattle H: have horns

(d) Many cows have horns.

(e) Every cow has horns.

(f) Each cow has horns.

2. Symbolize the following. Classify the resulting expressions as statements, open sentences, or neither. Specify the domain.

(a) y is green.

(b) the real number a.

(c) the green cow.

(d) the cow in the book is green.

(e) all cows.

(f) there is a green cow.

(g) all cows are green.

3. Explain why the following argument can be tested by considering the quantified expressions as statements and employing the statement calculus:

Either mathematics is not easy, or many students enjoy it. If logic is easy, then mathematics is not difficult. Thus logic is not easy if many students like mathematics.

4. Find the truth sets for the following open sentences. Take the domains to be the real numbers.

(a) $x + 1 = 0$

(b) $x^2 - 1 = 0$

(c) $|x| < 1$

(d) $x^2 < 1$

(e) $\cos^2\theta + \sin^2\theta = 1$

(f) $1 + \tan^2\theta = \sec^2\theta$

5. Note the relationships present between the truth sets established in Exercise 4.

(a) Which pair of truth sets contains one of the other truth sets?

(b) Which pairs of truth sets have no members in common?

(c) Which pairs of truth sets have members in common?

(d) Which pairs of truth sets have the same members?

§2   FUNCTION FORMULAS AND DIAGRAMS

The general concept of a function formula is that it must be some correct combination of statement functions and statement variables by the logical operators. That is, the operators discussed before will now be used to combine both statement variables and statement functions. The truth values will be established by an extension of the truth table techniques, but first we formalize the concept of a function formula.

Definition 5:   The following are *function formulas:*

(a) any statement variable formula.

(b) any statement function.

(c) $\sim f$ where f is a function formula.

(d) $f \; \theta \; g$ where f and g are function formulas and θ is one of the binary operators given in Chapter 1, §3.

(e) $(\forall x \; \epsilon \; \mathfrak{D}) f$ where f is a function formula.

(f) $(\exists x \; \epsilon \; \mathfrak{D}) f$ where f is a function formula.

(g) no expression is a function formula unless it is arrived at by the above recursive rules.

The establishment of truth value for a function formula requires that the formula be a statement. This will be the case when and only when all the variables are quantified, that is, when they fall within the scope of a related quantifier. The *scope* of a quantifier that occurs in a function formula is taken to be the quantifier and the smallest function formula immediately following the quantifier. This is illustrated in the following diagram by the indications of the scope of the universal quantifiers. The student should establish the scope of the existential quantifiers.

$$(\forall x)\ (P(x)\ \Rightarrow\ (\exists y)\ Q(y))$$

$$\underbrace{\hspace{5cm}}_{\text{scope}}$$

$$(\forall x)\ P(x)\ \Rightarrow\ (\exists y)\ Q(y)$$

$$\underbrace{\hspace{2.5cm}}_{\text{scope}}$$

$$(\forall x)\ (\exists y)\ (P(x)\ \lor\ Q(y))\ \Rightarrow\ R(x)$$

$$\underbrace{\hspace{6cm}}_{\text{scope}}$$

A function formula is a statement when each individual variable is within the scope of some quantifier that uses this individual variable. When an occurrence of an individual variable is within the scope of a quantifier that involves this particular variable, then this occurrence is said to be *bound*. The occurrence of an individual variable is said to be *free* when and only when it is not bound. In the above three formulas all occurrences of y are bound, and the x occurrences in the first two formulas are all bound. In the third formula the first occurrence of x and the occurrence of y are bound, whereas the $R(x)$ occurrence of x is free.

In case all the individual variables present in a function formula are bound, then we know that the expression has its truth value established by the truth values of the component statements. In this situation the truth table techniques established in the statement calculus supply us with the structure that we need. For example, $((\forall x)\ P(x)\ \land\ (\exists x)\ Q(x))\ \Rightarrow\ ((\forall x)\ P(x))$ is a tautology simply because it is a statement expressive of the form $(p\ \land\ q)\ \Rightarrow\ p$. The techniques we need to develop are the ones that deal with quantifiers that extend in scope over operators. That is $(\forall x)\ (P(x)\ \land\ Q(x))\ \Rightarrow\ (\forall x)\ P(x)$ is intuitively a tautology, but the statement calculus is not general enough to justify this conclusion. We now initiate this analysis by introducing the diagram method.

The quantified statement formulas may be investigated by diagrams of their truth sets. The process is not as mechanical as the truth table approach to statement variables, but it should prove more interesting. The techniques established will be sufficient to deal with the argument forms of classical logic and nearly all the problems that mathematicians encounter. The method will tend to be unsatisfactory when large numbers of different statement formulas are present simply because it is difficult to draw general diagrams for numerous set collections.

The statement calculus was developed with the technique of truth tables and no formal system derivations were included. Likewise the function calculus will be developed with a technique that utilizes diagrams of truth sets and no formal system of rules of inference will be derived. The student is encouraged to continue his logic studies to include formal systems, but such a study would be beyond the scope of this material.

The diagram method was originally introduced by the English logician John Venn (1834 – 1883) and the diagrams are usually referred to as Venn diagrams. A statement function is always given in relation to a particular domain of discussion, and the domain is thus broken down into two disjoint sets – – – the truth set and the false set. This is illustrated usually with a rectangle representing the domain and an inner oval that represents the truth set. For example $P(x)$ over a domain $\mathfrak{D}$ would diagram as in figure 2, with $\mathfrak{D}$ representing the domain and P the truth set of $P(x)$.

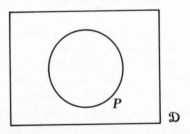

Fig. 2

To indicate that $(\forall x)\ P(x)$ is known to be true, the region of the domain that can not have members present is shaded out. (See figure 3.) The indication device that illustrates the knowledge of $(\exists x)\ P(x)$ is a cross that shows that the truth set of $P(x)$ is known to be non-empty. (See figure 4.)

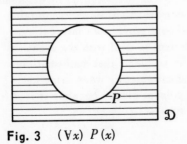

Fig. 3 $(\forall x)\ P(x)$

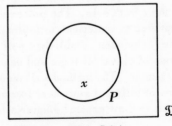

Fig. 4 $(\exists x)\ P(x)$

88

In case the function formula includes two statement functions, the diagram (see figure 5) is originally drawn to illustrate all possible situations. That is, if $P(x)$ and $Q(x)$ are present, then the diagram should show regions for points (1), in neither truth set; (2) and (3), in each of the truth sets singularly; and (4), in both truth sets jointly. Likewise if three statement functions are present (see figure 6), then regions should be indicated for (1) none of the truth sets; (2), (3) and (4), each truth set singularly; (5), (6) and (7), each pair of truth sets without elements of the third; and (8), all of the truth sets. The same general requirements hold for four statement functions, or five, etc.; but after four it becomes difficult to draw a reasonable figure that satisfies the specifications. (See figure 7.) The numbers in the regions will be used in parts of the later discussion to indicate the particular regions intended, so they are given here for reference.

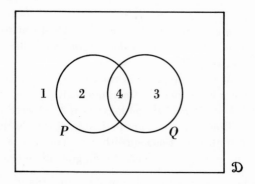

Fig. 5

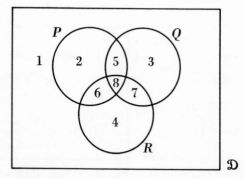

Fig. 6

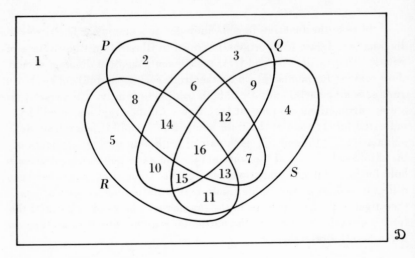

Fig. 7

Classical logic is interested in four function formulas, and we use these forms to explain the details of the diagram method. The first form is *universal affirmative*, $(\forall x)\ (P(x) \Rightarrow Q(x))$. In case we need to diagram knowledge that this statement is true, then every value a of the individual variable x must give the true statement $P(a) \Rightarrow Q(a)$. The only way that $P(a) \Rightarrow Q(a)$ could be false is if $P(a)$ were true and $Q(a)$ were false. Thus any a can not be inside of $P(x)$'s truth set and outside of $Q(x)$'s truth set. Consequently we shade out this region. No other knowledge is given, so we have the diagram shown in figure 8.

In a similar manner, knowledge of the falseness of $(\forall x)\ (P(x) \Rightarrow Q(x))$ would assure us that there must be an element in the previously described region. This is indicated in figure 9 by a cross that illustrates that the truth set of $P(x)$ that is outside of the truth set of $Q(x)$ is known to be non-null.

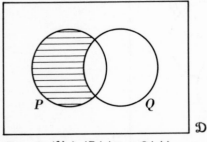

Fig. 8 $(\forall x)\ (P(x) \Rightarrow Q(x))$

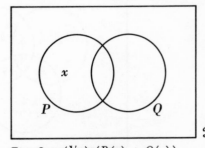

Fig. 9 $\sim(\forall x)\ (P(x) \Rightarrow Q(x))$

The other three forms from classical logic are *universal negative, particular affirmative* and *particular negative.* Historically the four forms are assigned the vowels *A, E, I* and *O* from *affirmo* and *nego.* Details and discussions will be supplied later, but the forms and their negatives are given here for reference. The student should verify the diagrams.

A: Universal affirmative and its negation (figures 10 and 11).

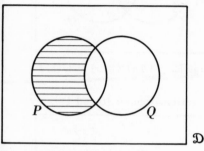

Fig. 10 $(\forall x)\,(P(x) \Rightarrow Q(x))$ **Fig. 11** $\sim(\forall x)\,(P(x) \Rightarrow Q(x))$

E: Universal negative and its negation (figures 12 and 13).

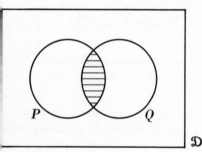 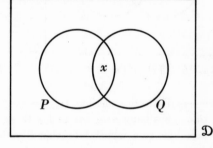

Fig. 12 $(\forall x)\,(P(x) \Rightarrow \sim Q(x))$ **Fig. 13** $\sim(\forall x)\,(P(x) \Rightarrow \sim Q(x))$

I: Particular affirmative and its negation (figures 14 and 15).

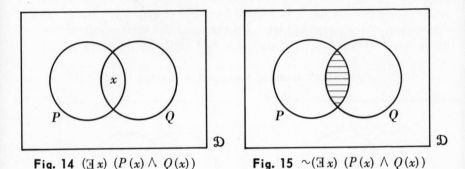

Fig. 14 $(\exists x)\ (P(x) \wedge Q(x))$

Fig. 15 $\sim(\exists x)\ (P(x) \wedge Q(x))$

O: Particular negative and its negation (figures 16 and 17).

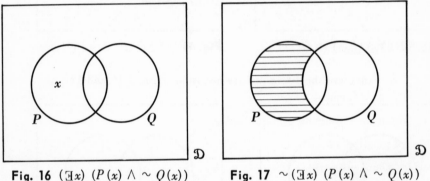

Fig. 16 $(\exists x)\ (P(x) \wedge \sim Q(x))$

Fig. 17 $\sim(\exists x)\ (P(x) \wedge \sim Q(x))$

There are obvious relationships between the forms and their negations, but before we proceed with an analysis of inferences we should note how to symbolize language sentences.

The symbol $(\forall x)\ (P(x) \Rightarrow Q(x))$ is the immediate translation of the sentence "All pythons are quarrelsome," but it is also the translation of "No python is nonquarrelsome," "No nonquarrelsome snake is a python," "All nonquarrelsome snakes are not pythons," and "It is false that any python is nonquarrelsome." The equivalence of the translations is more immediate when the example sentences are diagrammed. A typical error is the translation of "protagonists are quotable," as $(\forall x)$ $(P(x) \wedge Q(x))$. But the formula $(\forall x)\ (P(x) \wedge Q(x))$ diagrams (figure 5) as all regions except number 4 being shaded out, and this is not the intended meaning. To further illustrate, "All swans are white" does not mean that everything is a swan and everything is white.

Universal negation, $(\forall x)\,(P(x) \Rightarrow\, \sim Q(x))$ is the translation of "all pythons are nonquarrelsome" and the variations as given in the previous paragraph with "non" supplied in the proper positions. That is, "All P is non-Q", "No P is Q", "No Q is P", "All Q is non-P", and "It is false that some P is Q".

The sentences of the I and O form are basically of the form of an assertion of a particular instance or a statement to the effect that it is impossible for certain truth sets to be empty. Thus the I form is the translation of "Some P is Q", "Some Q is P" and "It is false that no P is Q". Likewise the O form is the translation of "Some P is not Q", "Some not Q is P" and "It is false that all P is Q".

EXERCISES (§ 2.)

1. Translate the following sentences and classify them as either A, E, I, or O forms.

(a) Any nonpeculiar thing is not quaint.

(b) All peculiar things are not quaint.

(c) No nonpeculiar thing is quaint.

(d) Some nonpeculiar thing is quaint.

(e) No quaint thing is peculiar.

(f) Some quaint thing is peculiar.

(g) It is false that no quaint thing is peculiar.

(h) It is false that all quaint things are peculiar.

2. (a) Draw a Venn diagram for representing five general predicate symbols P, Q, R, S, and T. (*Hint:* use a doughnut-like oval for T with the center at upper intersection of R and S's boundary in the given four predicate Venn diagrams.)

(b) Try to draw a general Venn diagram for six predicates.

(c) Draw a Venn diagram representing P, Q, R, S, and T under the given information $(\forall x)\,((Q(x) \wedge R(x)) \Rightarrow T(x))$.

3. Consider the alternate diagram method of just listing the possible regions. That is;

   I $(\sim P,\ \sim Q)$: _____

   II $(P,\ \sim Q)$: _____

   III $(\sim P,\ Q)$: _____

   IV $(P,\ Q)$: _____

For this technique we have:

Universal affirmative:

   I: _____   II: //////   III: _____   IV: _____

Particular affirmative:

   I: _____   II: x III: _____   IV: _____

Diagram with this alternate technique:

(a) Universal negative.

(b) Particular negative.

4. Detail the technique discussed in Exercise 3 for problems with:

(a) Three statement functions present.

(b) Four statement functions present.

(c) Five statement functions present.

(d) N statement functions present.

5. Sketch diagrams that illustrate knowledge of the truthfulness of the following:

(a) $(\forall x)\ (Px \vee Qx)$

(b) $(\forall x)\ (Px\ /\ Qx)$

(c) $(\exists x)\ (Px \downarrow Qx)$

(d) $(\forall x)\ (Px \wedge Qx)$

(e) $(\forall x)\ (Px \veebar Qx)$

(f) $(\forall x)\ (Px \downarrow Qx)$

(g) $(\forall x)\ (Px <\Rightarrow Qx)$

6. Explain the difficulty in drawing diagrams that illustrate knowledge of the truthfulness of the following:

(a) $(\exists x)\ (Px \lor Qx)$

(b) $(\exists x)\ (Px\ /\ Qx)$

(c) $(\exists x)\ (Px\ \underline{\lor}\ Qx)$

(d) $(\exists x)\ (Px \Rightarrow Qx)$

(e) $(\exists x)\ (Px <\Rightarrow Qx)$

7. Sketch diagrams that illustrate knowledge of the falseness of the following:

(a) Exercise 5. (a), (b) and (c)

(b) Exercise 6. (a), (b), (c), (d), and (e)

8. Translate the following sentences into logical symbols.

(a) All mathematics students are studious.

(b) Only mathematics students are studious.

(c) All dinners include coffee or tea.

(d) Real numbers are rational only if they are not irrational.

(e) Real numbers might be negative.

(f) Real numbers can not be imaginary.

(g) Prime integers or odd integers are not divisible by four.

(h) Quadrilaterals are singularly convex or concave.

§3 DIAGRAMS, INFERENCE AND SYLLOGISMS

We are interested in the relations between logical forms — — specifically, when is a particular form a consequence of one or more related forms. The analysis of arguments depends on the ability to recognize or establish these valid statement relationships. In the event that the argument involves basically statements and operators, then the statement calculus and truth tables supply the analytical techniques. In a like manner, the diagram method of testing inferences will be the basic device used in the analysis of quantified open sentences.

A function formula is said to be *implied* by a collection of function formulas when its diagram is given by the diagramming of the collection. For example, the argument,

> All men are fallible
>
> All kings are men
>
> Therefore all kings are fallible

would symbolize as:

$$(\forall x) \ (Mx \Rightarrow Fx)$$
$$(\forall x) \ (Kx \Rightarrow Mx)$$
$$\therefore \ (\forall x) \ (Kx \Rightarrow Fx) \ .$$

Here the domain of discussion is the collection of all humans; and the predicate variables M, F, K are respectively: "is a man", "is fallible", "is a king". In the diagram analysis, we would first indicate the information given by the first two statements, i.e., the two premises. If the diagram then includes the diagram of the assertion, then we would conclude that the inference is valid.

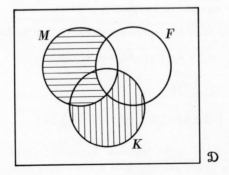

Fig. 18

In figure 18 the horizontal shading is from the first statement "All men are fallible" and the vertical shading is from the second given sentence. Since the region of K that is outside of F is now shaded out, we conclude that the assertion "All kings are fallible" is a valid inference. That is, the diagram of the conclusion is included in the diagramming of the premises; thus the given information implies the conclusion.

Now consider the statement: "If there exist large and powerful automobiles, then there exist large automobiles and there exist powerful automobiles". We know intuitively that this simple sentence is true, but the statement calculus is not able to justify the truthfulness. The form is "$(\exists x)\ (Lx \wedge Px) \Rightarrow ((\exists x)\ Lx \wedge (\exists x)\ Px)$". The statement calculus would have to symbolize the sentence as $p \Rightarrow (q \wedge r)$. This is not a tautology, so the analytical techniques of the statement calculus would not be sufficient to justify the truthfulness of the sentence. But if we diagram the given information "there exist large and powerful automobiles", we see that a cross must be placed in the general truth set that is common to the sets L and P.

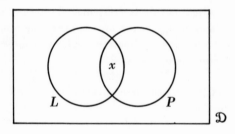

Fig. 19

The diagram in figure 19 includes the information that there is an x within the L set, that is, $(\exists x)Lx$. Likewise it indicates an x within the P set, and we correctly conclude $(\exists x)Lx \wedge (\exists x)Px$.

The diagram method readily gives very useful information about the negation operator and the quantifiers. The usual interpretation of these relationships is that "a negation operator reverses the quantifier when it goes across them". This memory device is the interpretation of the following relationships:

$$\sim (\forall x)\ Px \Longleftrightarrow (\exists x)\sim Px$$

$$\sim (\exists x)\ Px \Longleftrightarrow (\forall x)\sim Px$$

To show the first biconditional relationship we need to justify
$\sim (\forall x)\ Px \Rightarrow (\exists x)\sim Px$ and $(\exists x)\sim Px \Rightarrow \sim (\forall x)\ Px$. The implications are given by the diagram in figure 20.

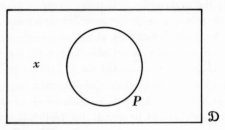

Fig. 20

To conclude the first implication, the diagram of $\sim (\forall x)\ Px$ is arrived at by observing that the region outside of the P set can not be all shaded out. The x indicates this information. This is also the diagram of $(\exists x)\sim Px$. An interchange of the order of the considerations of the diagramming gives the second implication, and we conclude that the first biconditional relationship is valid.

The validity of the second bicondition relationship is given by the diagram in figure 21.

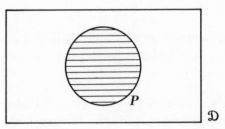

Fig. 21

The negation of quantifiers is especially important to mathematical proofs. For instance to show that something is not universally true, we have to show the existence of counter example, i.e., a single example for which the statement is not true. In particular, to show that not all functions are continuous, we need to illustrate only one noncontinuous function. Correspondingly to show that there does not exist a real number whose square is negative, we need to prove that all real numbers are such that their square is non-negative. Some students have difficulty with counter example (denial of a universal), and universal denial proofs. The trouble is usually due to a misunderstanding of the simple logical relationship between negation and quantifiers.

Another basic mathematical concept that requires negation and quantifiers is a proof that involves a discontinuous function. The definition of a continuous function employs a two-place predicate variable, so we will have to delay its discussion until a later section.

Traditionally the study of logic has included an analysis of syllogisms. These important arguments are in structure combinations of the historical forms. A *syllogism* is an argument composed of three *A, E, I,* or *O* statements with the requirement that: (i) the first two statements are the premises or given information, (ii) the last statement is the conclusion, (iii) the first two statements are connected by a statement function called the middle term, (iv) the first and last statements are related by means of a major term statement function, (v) the second and last statements are related with the minor term statement function, and (vi) the first and second statement functions in the conclusion are the minor and major terms respectively. Under these formation rules we can observe that there are only four possible figures that illustrate a syllogistic format.

I:	middle	major		II:	major	middle
	minor	middle			minor	middle
	minor	major			minor	major

III:	middle	major		IV:	major	middle
	middle	minor			middle	minor
	minor	major			minor	major

For example, the argument given about fallible kings in the first of this section is a syllogism with a type I figure format. The statement formulas *Fx, Mx* and *Kx* are respectively the major, middle, and

and minor terms. The specification of particular syllogism requires the figure format identification and the logical form of the three statements. To illustrate, the fallible kings argument is completely classified by I-*AAA*, and an example of IV-*EAO* is as follows.

> All horses are not fishes
>
> All fishes are swimmers
>
> Therefore some swimmers are not horses.

The classification IV-*EAO* is immediate with the following symbolization.

$$(\forall x) \ (Hx \Rightarrow \sim Fx)$$
$$(\forall x) \ (Fx \Rightarrow Sx)$$
$$\therefore (\exists x) \ (Sx \wedge \sim Hx)$$

The diagram method supplies the answer to the validity decision about this argument form. That is, the inference is not valid. The additional information that there are fishes is needed to make the argument valid. It could happen that no x is an Fx, so the argument is invalid according to our system. The diagram is given in figure 22.

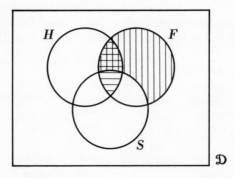

Fig. 22

The theory of syllogisms is much more involved than this material indicates. The basic concepts of subject-predicate requirements and distribution of terms are fundamental to the formal theory and we have not discussed any of these points. The classification of syllogisms started with Aristotle and the results of logicians past and present have culminated in an involved theory that seems to be too elaborate for every day employment. The diagram method of testing inferences is independent of the specialized rules of syllogistic testing, and it has the advantages of having wide application and ease of remembrance. The diagram method will establish the validity of all the valid syllogisms.

In general there are 256 possible syllogisms and only 15 are valid inference forms. Each of the three statements may be independently one of the four basic forms, thus each figure format will allow $4 \cdot 4 \cdot 4$ or 64 possible syllogisms. Then the four possible formats give a total of $4 \cdot 64$ or 256. The 15 valid forms for the respective figure formats are

I: *AAA, EAE, AII, EIO*

II: *EAE, AEE, EIO, AOO*

III: *IAI, AII, OAO, EIO*

IV: *AEE, IAI, EIO.*

EXERCISES (§ 3.)

1. Find the negations of the following:

(a) All rectangles are quadrilaterals.

(b) Some functions are continuous.

(c) There are differentiable functions.

(d) All real numbers are rational or irrational, but not both.

(e) For all real numbers x, exactly one of the following is true: (i) $x > 0$, (ii) $x < 0$, or (iii) $x = 0$.

(f) Any neighborhood of the origin contains the point $\propto$.

(g) There exists a neighborhood of the origin that contains the point $\propto$.

(h) No neighborhood of the origin fails to contain the point $\propto$.

(i) All neighborhoods of the origin fail to contain the point $\propto$.

2. Historically the valid forms of syllogisms have associated names with the vowels present in the names used to suggest the form, e.g., I-EIO and the related Ferio

(a) Verify by the diagram method the four valid figure I syllogisms, viz., Barbara, Celarent, Darii, Ferio

(b) Verify the valid figure II syllogisms, viz., Cesare, Camestres, Festino, Baroco

(c) Verify the valid figure III syllogisms, viz., Disamis, Datisi, Bocardo, Ferison

(d) Verify the valid figure IV syllogisms, viz., Camenes, Dimarisa, Fresison.

3. One rule about syllogisms is that "if both premises are negative (EE, EO, OE, or OO) then no valid conclusion is possible". Show that the rule is correct for the following restricted groups.

(a) Figure I and EE

(b) Figure II and EO

(c) Figure III and OE

(d) Figure IV and OO.

4. Another rule about valid syllogisms is that "if one premise is negative (E or O), then the conclusion must be negative". Show that the rule is correct for the following restricted groups. (Assume the rule stated in Exercise 3.)

(a) Figure I with an A conclusion

(b) Figure II with an E conclusion

(c) Figure III with an I conclusion

(d) Figure IV with an O conclusion.

5. To the syllogism rules formulated by medieval logicians, one additional rule must be added, namely, "Two universal (AA, AE, EA, EE) premises can not validly conclude a particular (I or O) statement" Explain why the following traditional forms would not be considered valid. Specify an additional premise about the existence of certain individuals that would be required to make a valid argument.

(a) Figure I: Barbari, Celaront

(b) Figure II: Cesaro, Camestros

(c) Figure III: Darapti, Felapton

(d) Figure V: Bramantip, Fesapo, Camenos.

6. Test the following syllogisms authored by Lewis Carroll. The last statement is the conclusion.

(a) Gold is heavy;
Nothing but gold will silence him.
Nothing light will silence him.

(b) All lions are fierce;
Some lions do not drink coffee.
Some creatures that drink coffee are not fierce.

(c) All wasps are unfriendly;
No puppies are unfriendly.
Puppies are not wasps.

(d) Some pillows are soft;
No pokers are soft.
Some pokers are not pillows.

(e) Every eagle can fly;
Some pigs can not fly.
Some pigs are not eagles.

(f) No frogs are poetical;
Some ducks are unpoetical.
Some ducks are not frogs.

7. Show that the following relationships are valid by investigating diagrams.

(a) $(\forall x)\ (Px \wedge Qx) \Longleftrightarrow ((\forall x)\ Px \wedge (\forall x)\ Qx)$

(b) $(\exists x)\ (Px \vee Qx) \Longleftrightarrow ((\exists x)\ Px \vee (\exists x)\ Qx)$

(c) $(\exists x)\ (Px \wedge Qx) \Longrightarrow ((\exists x)\ Px \wedge (\exists x)\ Qx)$

(d) $((\forall x)\ Px \vee (\forall x)\ Qx) \Longrightarrow (\forall x)\ (Px \vee Qx)$

(e) $(\forall x)\ (Px \Longrightarrow Qx) \Longrightarrow ((\forall x)\ Px \Longrightarrow (\forall x)\ Qx)$

(f) $\sim(\forall x)\ Px \iff (\exists x) \sim Px$

(g) $\sim(\exists x) \sim Px \iff (\forall x)\ Px$

(h) $\sim(\forall x) \sim Px \iff (\exists x)\ Px$

(i) $(\forall x) \sim Px \iff \sim (\exists x)\ Px$

(j) $(\forall x)\ (Px \Rightarrow Qx) \Rightarrow ((\exists x)\ Px \Rightarrow (\exists x)\ Qx)$

8. Assume that the algebra of statement operators applies to statement functions as well as to statement variables and show that the relationships expressed in exercise 7(a) and (g) can be used to derive 7(b).

9. Explain why the following are not valid.

(a) $((\exists x)\ Px \land (\exists x)\ Qx) \Rightarrow (\exists x)\ (Px \land Qx)$

(b) $(\forall x)\ (Px \lor Qx) \Rightarrow ((\forall x)\ Px \lor (\forall x)\ Qx)$

(c) $(\forall x)\ Px \Rightarrow (\exists x)\ Px$

§4 FURTHER INFERENCE

This section includes the relationship between statement variables and quantifiers along with further points about the diagram method. We will assume that the statement variable operators apply to the statement functions as well as to statement variables and that the algebraic relationships developed in Part I are valid in the function formulas.

The new problem is the analysis of a function formula that contains both statement variables and statement functions. The simplest situation is a quantifier that has only a statement variable present in its scope, namely, $(\forall x)\ p$ or $(\exists x)\ p$. Since $\tau((\forall x)p) = T$ if and only if all substitutions of x into p give a true statement, we see that $\tau((\forall x)p) = T$ if and only if $\tau(p) = T$. The existential situation has a corresponding argument and we have the following

$$(\forall x)p \iff p$$
$$(\exists x)p \iff p.$$

Now consider the combination with a quantifier that has a statement variable and a statement function within its scope. For example, $(\exists x)\ (p \Rightarrow Qx)$ is equivalent to $p \Rightarrow (\exists x)\ Qx$. The proof of this assertion is given by an investigation of a sequence of steps that are justified by previous results.

Theorem a $(\exists x)\ (p \Rightarrow Qx) \Leftrightarrow (p \Rightarrow (\exists x)\ Qx)$

Proof: $(\exists x)\ (p \Rightarrow Qx) \Leftrightarrow {\sim}\,{\sim}\,(\exists x)\ (p \Rightarrow Qx)$
$\qquad\qquad\qquad\ \Leftrightarrow {\sim}\,(\forall x)\ {\sim}\,(p \Rightarrow Qx)$
$\qquad\qquad\qquad\ \Leftrightarrow {\sim}\,(\forall x)\ (p \wedge {\sim}\,Qx)$
$\qquad\qquad\qquad\ \Leftrightarrow {\sim}((\forall x)p \wedge (\forall x)\ {\sim}\,Qx)$ (Exercise 7)
$\qquad\qquad\qquad\ \Leftrightarrow {\sim}\,(p \wedge {\sim}\,(\exists x)\ Qx)$
$\qquad\qquad\qquad\ \Leftrightarrow (p \Rightarrow (\exists x)\ Qx).$

Not all proofs for this type of formula are constructible with sequences of biconditions. The following theorem illustrates a proof that breaks the biconditional into two implications.

Theorem b $(\forall x)\ (p \Rightarrow Qx) \Leftrightarrow (p \Rightarrow (\forall x)\ Qx)$

Proof: $(\forall x)(p \Rightarrow Qx) \Rightarrow {\sim}\,(\exists x)\ {\sim}\,(p \Rightarrow Qx)$
$\qquad\qquad\qquad\ \Rightarrow {\sim}\,(\exists x)(p \wedge {\sim}\,Qx)$
$\qquad\qquad\qquad\ \Rightarrow {\sim}\,((\exists x)p \wedge (\exists x)\ {\sim}\,Qx)$ (Exercise 7)
$\qquad\qquad\qquad\ \Rightarrow {\sim}\,(p \wedge {\sim}\,(\forall x)\ Qx)$
$\qquad\qquad\qquad\ \Rightarrow (p \Rightarrow (\forall x)\ Qx)$
$\quad (p \Rightarrow (\forall x)\ Qx) \Rightarrow ({\sim}\,p \vee (\forall x)\ Qx)$
$\qquad\qquad\qquad\ \Rightarrow ((\forall x)\ {\sim}\,p \vee (\forall x)\ Qx)$
$\qquad\qquad\qquad\ \Rightarrow (\forall x)({\sim}\,p \vee Qx)$
$\qquad\qquad\qquad\ \Rightarrow (\forall x)(p \Rightarrow Qx)$

Another point about the diagram method needs some mention. That is the idea of linked crosses. In the diagramming of an existential quantified statement, we have on occasion the problem of inserting a cross and the location is not completely established. Consider the following argument, "Since all mathematics uses abstract thoughts, all abstract thoughts employ symbols, and there is an abstract thought; so mathematics or abstract thoughts exist". The symbolization and diagram of this argument is given in figure 23.

$$(\forall x)\,(Mx \;\Rightarrow\; Ax)$$
$$(\forall x)\,(Ax \;\Rightarrow\; Sx)$$
$$(\exists x)\;\;Ax$$
$$\overline{}$$
$$\therefore\;(\exists x)\,(Mx \;\vee\; Sx)$$

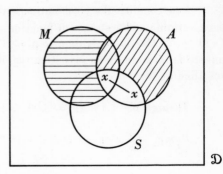

Fig. 23

The linked crosses in figure 23 indicate that there is an element someplace in the two regions and we do not have sufficient information to conclude the exact location. Even though our given information is not completely specific, we are able to verify that the argument's conclusion is valid.

We might note that it is a good practice to diagram the shaded information first. In this way the placing of crosses will be more restrictive and the number of linked crosses will be minimized.

A fundamental error is the confusion of crosses. The argument "There are short rich people and there are short famous people, therefore there are famous rich people" is clearly not valid. The premises could be true, but if every short rich person is not famous, then the conclusion would be false. The error in a diagram analysis that would lead to the incorrect conclusion of validity is a simple mistake in identity of the crosses, especially if a cross is linked to an unrelated cross. The correct and an incorrect diagram for this argument are shown in figures 24 and 25.

We now have essentially two techniques of analysis at our disposal. They are the diagram method and the proof concept that employs results arrived at with the diagram method. For simple arguments, the diagram method is the easiest, but more complicated forms are occasionally better analyzed with algebraic manipulation.

106

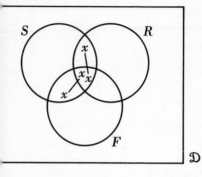

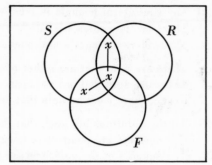

Fig. 24   Correct   **Fig. 25**   Incorrect

EXERCISES (§4.)

1. Justify the steps in the proof of:

(a) Theorem a.

(b) Theorem b.

2. Prove the following theorems

(a) $(\forall x)\,(Qx \Rightarrow p) \iff ((\exists x)\,Qx \Rightarrow p)$

(b) $(\exists x)\,(Qx \Rightarrow p) \iff (\forall x)\,(Qx \Rightarrow p)$

(c) $(\forall x)\,(Qx \land p) \iff ((\forall x)\,Qx \land p)$

(d) $(\exists x)\,(Qx \land p) \iff (p \land (\exists x)\,Qx)$

3. Test the following arguments:

(a) All differentiable functions are continuous.
    There exists a differentiable function.
    Thus, there exists a continuous function.

(b) There is a solution larger than 1 or less than −1.
    No solution is greater than 1.
    Therefore there is a solution less than −1.

(c) All differentiable functions are continuous.
    There exists a non-differentiable function.
    Therefore, there exists a non-continuous function.

(d) Any equilateral triangle is isosceles.
There are isosceles triangles.
Thus, there are equilateral triangles.

(e) There are sets that are either open or closed.
There are sets that are not open.
Hence, there must be sets that are open.

(f) All the solutions are such that their square is non-zero when the numbers are positive or negative.
The squares of the solutions are zero.
Consequently no solution is negative when it is not positive.

4. Determine the truth value of the following formulas.

(a) $((\exists x) Px \wedge (\forall x) (Px \wedge Qx)) \Rightarrow (\exists x) Qx$

(b) $(\forall x)(Px \wedge \sim Qx) \vee \sim (\exists x) Px \vee (\exists x) Qx.$

(*Hint:* use a few algebraic relationships to change the form.)

(c) $(\exists x)(Px \vee \sim Qx) \wedge (\forall x) \sim Px \wedge (\forall x) Qx.$

(*Hint:* $\tau(p \wedge \sim p) = \text{F}.$)

(d) $\sim (\exists x)(Px) \vee (\exists x)(Px \wedge \sim Qx) \vee (\exists x) Qx.$

Chapter 6

THE FUNCTION CALCULUS
OF MANY VARIABLES

A large part of mathematics involves expressions of the type "for all $---$, there is $---$," and "there is $---$ such that $---$." The fundamental concept is that two things are interconnected in a general quantified manner. Recall that the statement calculus analyzed the basic statement structure and that the function calculus of one variable was primarily concerned with subject and predicate interaction. Consequently we need to extend our material to include relationships between two or more connected groups of subjects. It might seem odd to discuss a "two-place predicate," but the idea of multiple-place predicate variables is the natural extension. That is, expressions of the type "$x > y$" will be said to relate the concepts x and y by the predicate relationship "less than." The symbolization is "$L(x,y)$." Formally the connection is a relation and not a predicate, but we will use the later terminology as an extension of the one-place predicate concepts.

§1 MULTIPLE PLACE STATEMENT FUNCTIONS AND PRODUCT SETS

In this section we take the natural extension of predicate variables to include many-place predicate variables, and we introduce the concept of product sets. So first of all we formalize the definitions of general statement functions and function formulas.

An *n-place predicate variable* is a symbol for a concept that relates n individual variables. Now, the definition of a *statement function* is extended to: a collection of symbols for an open sentence involving any finite number of individual variables that are interrelated by means of an n-place predicate. Likewise the definition of a *function formula* is extended to allow the inclusion of n-place statement functions.

The concepts of scope of quantifiers and bound and free variables should be reviewed. We can see that the function formula $(\forall x)P(x, y)$ contains a free variable y and a bound variable x. Recall that a function formula symbolizes a statement when all the individual variables are bound. This is the case in either $(\forall x)(\exists y)\ P(x,y)$, $(\forall y)(\forall x)\ P(x,y)$, $(\exists y)(\forall x)\ P(x,y)$ or $(\forall x)(\forall y)\ P(x,y)$. We can examine the truth value and the truth function τ, but the substitution instances involve product sets. Consequently we discuss product sets first.

The product set consists of ordered pairs. An *ordered pair* is formally two elements — — a pair, with the order specified. The first element of the pair is termed the first coordinate and the second element is called the second coordinate of the pair. The concept is not foreign to anyone who knows analytic geometry; the coordinate plane is in fact a set of ordered pairs of real numbers. Here we will use a corresponding notation (x,y) to indicate an ordered pair, and generally speaking (x,y) will be different from (y,x). They are the same pair, x and y; but the order is different.

Now we are able to formally define a product set. That is, the *product set* formed with two sets A and B is the set of all ordered pairs formed with the first coordinate from the A set and the second coordinate from the B set. The notation is $A \times B$. For example, the coordinate plane studied in analytic geometry is simply the product set formed by the real number set producted with the real number set. We are interested in product sets involving our domain of discussion, so our analysis will deal with product sets $\mathfrak{D} \times \mathfrak{D}$.

Recall that our domains might be sets like "all humans," and "all poetical frogs." So our product sets will be considerably more general than the usual coordinate plane, even though it is a good memory device to keep in mind.

In order to classify the truth value of function formulas with a two-place statement function and no free variables, we employ the product set $\mathfrak{D} \times \mathfrak{D}$. Intuitively the truthfulness of $(\forall x)(\forall y)\ P(x,y)$ would require that "for any x and for any y, $P(x,y)$ has to be true." We establish this as a formal requirement: $\tau((\forall x)(\forall y)\ P(x,y)) = T$ if and only if any ordered pair (x,y) in $\mathfrak{D} \times \mathfrak{D}$ is such that $\tau(P(x,y)) = T$. For instance, "Everybody sees everybody as peculiar," would symbolize as the above function formula. We assert that it is true if and only if any particular pair of people (x,y) is such that x sees y as peculiar. In $\mathfrak{D} \times \mathfrak{D}$, if the statement is true, we observe that the truth set of $P(x,y)$ must be the complete product set. The statement function $P(x,y)$ is "x sees y as peculiar".

The statement, "There is somebody whom everyone sees as peculiar," has a symbol representation of $(\exists y)(\forall x)\ P(x,y)$. Note that we conclude that this assertion is true under the provision that some one individual seems peculiar to everyone. In terms of the product set, this means that there is a particular y_o such that for any ordered pair (x,y_o), $\tau(P(x,y_o)) = T$. In this discussion, the ordered pair (x,y_o) is a single ordered pair of individuals x and y_o. The x is a single unspecified individual, and the y_o is a single fixed individual. So when we note $\tau(P(x,y_o)) = T$, we are talking about a statement formed by a substitution of a single ordered pair into the statement function. This type of notation has its inherent confusing elements, but it is unavoidable without an elaborate notational structure.

The understanding of the truth set of $(\exists y)(\forall x)\ P(x,y)$ gives very useful information, i.e., the diagram of the truth set in $\mathcal{D} \times \mathcal{D}$ must contain at least a horizontal line whenever the statement is true. Here the domain of discussion $\mathcal{D}$ is the set of all individuals, and the x individual variable is considered in the usual way as the horizontal coordinate.

If we consider the requirements on the truth sets of $(\forall x)(\forall y)$ $P(x,y)$ and $(\exists y)(\forall x)\ P(x,y)$, we arrive at our first general relationship.

$$(\forall x)(\forall y)\ P(x,y) \Rightarrow (\exists y)(\forall x)\ P(x,y)$$

Now consider the statement "Everybody thinks somebody is peculiar". The symbolization is immediate: $(\forall x)(\exists y)\ P(x,y)$; but the truth set is somewhat complex. In $\mathcal{D} \times \mathcal{D}$ we observe that above every x, there must be some point (x,y) within the truth set. This would happen in case the truth set contained a horizontal line, but it could happen in truth sets that failed to contain a straight line. The truth set could be a snake-like curve without any loops, e.g., a sine curve; or it could be a disconnected set of dots scattered all over the product set. Mathematically speaking, the requirement is that a subset of the truth set give y as a function of x. Under these observations, we can conclude the following:

$$(\exists y)(\forall x)\ P(x,y) \Rightarrow (\forall x)(\exists y)\ P(x,y)$$

The statement "Somebody thinks somebody is peculiar" readily symbolizes as $(\exists x)\,(\exists y)\;P(x,y)$. For truthfulness, the truth set requirement is that there must exist at least one point within the truth set. With this observation we have the following:

$$(\forall x)\,(\exists y)\;P(x,y) \Rightarrow (\exists x)\,(\exists y)\;P(x,y)$$

Now contrast the previous statement with "Somebody seems peculiar to somebody". This means that there is an individual y, such that for some individual x, y seems peculiar to x. In symbols we have $(\exists y)\,(\exists x)\;P(x,y)$. The latter function formula is different from the one in the above paragraph, but the truth set requirements are the same. Namely, for truthfulness, the truth set can not be empty. This allows us to conclude that existential quantifiers commute, that is,

$$(\exists x)\,(\exists y)\;P(x,y) \Leftrightarrow (\exists y)\,(\exists x)\;P(x,y)$$

We can also observe that universal quantifiers commute. Consider the statements, "Everybody sees everybody as peculiar", and "Everybody seems peculiar to everybody". They have respective symbol expressions $(\forall x)\,(\forall y)\;P(x,y)$ and $(\forall y)\,(\forall x)\;P(x,y)$. The truth set requirements on both function formulas are the same — — that the truth set is the complete product set. Consequently we have the following:

$$(\forall x)\,(\forall y)\;P(x,y) \Leftrightarrow (\forall y)\,(\forall x)\;P(x,y)$$

Now consider the two statements "There is somebody that sees everyone as peculiar" and "Everybody seems peculiar to somebody". The respective function formulas are $(\exists x)\,(\forall y)\;P(x,y)$ and $(\forall y)\,(\exists x)\;P(x,y)$. An investigation of their truth sets gives the result that the first function formula implies the latter. The first truth set must contain a vertical line, and the second must contain a point (x,y) for any element y of the domain.

$$(\exists x)\,(\forall y)\;P(x,y) \Rightarrow (\forall y)\,(\exists x)\;P(x,y)$$

Before we compile the results into a reference chart, we introduce an alternate predicate to use as our example. Consider our domain of discussion as the set of integers, — — the whole numbers 0, 1, −1, 2, −2, 3, −3, etc. The relationship $P(x,y)$ is taken to be x precedes y, that is, x comes before y in the natural order of the integers. The various statements, their symbols, and their related implications are given below as a combination example. The letter "I" is used as an abbreviation of "integer" for space reasons. Actually only four of the statements are true about all integers, and three of the statements are true about the positive integers. It is left as an exercise to classify the sentences as true or false in regard to the domain of integers and the domain of positive integers.

$(\forall x)\,(\forall y)\ P(x,y)$ $\quad$ $<=>$ $\qquad$ $(\forall y)\,(\forall x)\ P(x,y)$

$(\exists y)\,(\forall x)\ P(x,y)$ $\qquad\qquad\qquad$ $(\exists x)\,(\forall y)\ P(x,y)$

$(\forall x)\,(\exists y)\ P(x,y)$ $\qquad\qquad\qquad$ $(\forall y)\,(\exists x)\ P(x,y)$

$(\exists x)\,(\exists y)\ P(x,y)$ $\quad$ $<=>$ $\qquad$ $(\exists y)\,(\exists x)\ P(x,y)$

Every I precedes every I $\quad<=>\quad$ Every I is preceded by every I.

Some I is preceded by every I $\qquad$ Some I precedes every I.

Every I precedes some I $\qquad$ Every I is preceded by some I.

Some I precedes some I $\quad<=>\quad$ Every I is preceded by some I.

("I" represents "integer")

Example: Consider the three integers, 2, 4, and 6 as our domain of discussion, and the following relations:

(a) $C(x,y)$: x and y have a common factor

(b) $E(x,y)$: $x \geqq y$ (x at least exceeds y)

(c) $F(x,y)$: y is a factor of x

(d) $D(x,y)$: x is a factor of y

(e) $G(x,y)$: $x - 2y \geqq -2$

(f) $H(x,y)$: $y - 2x \geqq -2$

(g) $I(x,y)$: $|x - 4| + y = 6$

(h) $J(x,y)$: $x + |y - 4| = 6$

(i) $K(x,y)$: $2y - x = 4$

(j) $L(x,y)$: $x + y = 14$

The product set consists of simply nine ordered pairs (2,2), (2,4), (2,6), . . . , (6,6); but it is best illustrated with a coordinate plane diagram.

$$\mathfrak{D} \textbf{ X } \mathfrak{D}: \quad \begin{array}{lll} \cdot(2,6) & \cdot(4,6) & \cdot(6,6) \\ \cdot(2,4) & \cdot(4,4) & \cdot(6,4) \\ \cdot(2,2) & \cdot(4,2) & \cdot(6,2) \end{array}$$

Now if we look at the truth sets of the various statement functions we can construct a large group of true statements. For instance, all the points (x,y) in the product set give, under substitution, a true statement $C(x,y)$. The product set is finite, so we can verify each ordered pair individually. With this observation, we conclude,

$$(\forall x)\, (\forall y)\ \ C(x,y)\ ;$$

and it is a trivial matter to write down the seven other forms implied by this statement. We also observe that $D(x,y)$ has a truth set composed of (2,6), (2,4), (2,2), (4,4) and (6,6). This yields both of the following conclusions.

$$(\exists x)\, (\forall y)\ \ D(x,y)$$

$$(\forall x)\, (\exists y)\ \ D(x,y)$$

Note that it is not the case that some y has any x as a factor, that is, $\tau((\exists y)(\forall x)\ D(x,y)) = \text{F}$.

A collection of true statements is given below; it would be a good exercise for the student to verify that each of them is the "strongest" true statement that can be established. By strongest, we mean that this list includes all the statements that are true, except for the true statements that are implied by ones in the stated list.

$$(\exists y)\, (\forall x)\ \ E(x,y), \quad (\exists x)\, (\forall y)\ \ E(x,y)$$

$$(\exists y)\, (\forall x)\ \ F(x,y), \quad (\forall y)\, (\exists x)\ \ F(x,y)$$

$$(\exists y)\, (\forall x)\, (x - 2y \geq -2)$$

$$(\exists x)\, (\forall y)\, (y - 2x \geq -2)$$

$$(\forall x)\, (\exists y)\, (\,|x - 4| + y = 6)$$

$$(\forall y)\, (\exists x)\, (x + |y - 4| = 6)$$

$$(\exists x)\, (\exists y)\, (x + y = 14)$$

EXERCISES (§ 1.)

1. In the group of statements about integers in this section:

(a) Which four statements are true about all integers?

(b) Which three statements are true about the positive integers?

2. In the group of statements about people considering people peculiar within this section, which statements are true?

3. Construct two statements, one false and one true, that show that an existential quantifier does not commute with a universal quantifier.

4. In the example in this section, demonstrate that each function formula is the "strongest" true one. That is, show that the function formula that immediately precedes it in the implication chart is not true.

5. Establish the true value, whenever possible, of the following. The domain of discussion is taken to be the set of real numbers.

(a) $(\forall x)(\exists y)(x + y = 1)$

(b) $(\forall x)(\exists y)(y = 1)$

(c) $(\forall \theta)(\forall \psi)(\sin^2\theta + \cos^2\theta = 1)$

(d) $(\exists x)(\forall y)(x + y = 1)$

(e) $(\forall x)(\forall y)(x^2 - y^2 = (x + y)(x - y))$

(f) $(\forall x)(\forall y)((x^2 - y^2)/(x + y)) = (x - y)$

(g) $(\forall \theta)(\forall \psi)(\sin(\theta - \psi) = \sin\theta \cos\psi - \cos\theta \sin\psi)$

(h) $(\forall x)(\exists y)(x^2 > y^2)$

(i) $(\exists x)(\forall y)(x^2 < y^2)$

(j) $(\exists x)(\forall y)(x^2 \leq y^2)$

6. To establish the following as true statements, what quantifiers should precede the equations? Specify your domain.

(a) $x^2 - 3x + 2 = 0$

(b) $y^2 = x^2$

(c) $\tan \theta = 1/\sec \theta$

(d) $\cos \theta/(1 - \sin \theta) = (1 + \sin \theta) / \cos \theta$

(e) $x^2 - y^2 = (x + y)(x - y)$

(f) $(x^2 - y^2)/(x - y) = (x + y)$

     7. Express in symbols the following mathematical definitions. Specify your domain.

(a) Limit of a function: given $\epsilon > 0$, there exists a $\delta > 0$ such that $|f(x) - L| < \epsilon$ whenever $|x - a| < \delta$.

(b) function, $f(x)$, continuous at a: For all positive numbers ϵ, there is a positive number δ with the property that $|x - a| < \delta$ only if $|f(x) - f(a)| < \epsilon$.

(c) function, $f(x)$, continuous on a set S: For any x in S and any $\epsilon > 0$, there exists a $\delta > 0$ such that $|f(x) - f(y)| < \epsilon$ whenever y is in S and $|x - y| < \delta$. (*Hint:* use more than two quantifiers)

(d) function, $f(x)$, uniformly continuous on a set S: For any $\epsilon > 0$, there exists a $\delta > 0$ such that $|f(x) - f(y)| < \epsilon$ whenever x and y are in S and $|x - y| < \delta$.

(e) sequence, $\{a_n\}$, convergent to A: For all $\epsilon > 0$, there exists an N such that $n > N$ implies $|a_n - A| < \epsilon$.

(f) a Cauchy sequence, $\{a_n\}$: For all $\epsilon > 0$, there is an N such that $|a_n - a_m| < \epsilon$ whenever m and n are larger than N.

     8. Consider a finite domain of discussion consisting of a, b, and c. Express the following as strings of conjunctions and disjunctions.

(a) $(\exists x)(\forall y)\ P(x,y)$

(b) $(\forall x)(\exists y)\ P(x,y)$

(c) $(\exists y)(\forall x)\ P(x,y)$

§2 OPERATIONS WITH QUANTIFIERS

We are now in a position to symbolize complex statements. All
we need is a few algebraic rules for rearrangement of quantifiers within
a function formula. Then a complex argument will lend itself to analysis
by a symbolization of the sentences, manipulation of the logical symbols
to a more simplified form and finally an analysis of the truth diagram.

The simplest manipulation of operators and quantifiers is the employment of the general negation rule, i.e., substitute the other quantifier when the negation operator crosses a quantifier. For example,
"Every integer does not precede some integer", "Every integer fails to
precede every integer", and "It is not the case that some integer precedes every integer" are all equivalent. This manipulation scheme can
be extended to make the negation cover all the statement variable operators, e.g. conjunction; and all types of seemingly complicated equivalent statements can result.

The negation of quantifiers preceding an implication is a very
important concept to mathematics. In the previous exercise group the
definition of a continuous function was given. That is in the domain
of positive numbers, $(\forall \epsilon)\, (\exists \delta)\, (\forall x)\, (\,|x - a| < \delta \Rightarrow |f(x) - f(a)|$
$< \epsilon)$. In case we wanted to prove that a function is not continuous at
a point, we would have to negate the above function formula. The re-
sult would be: $(\exists \epsilon)\, (\forall \delta)\, (\exists x)\, (\,|x - a| < \delta \wedge |f(x) - f(a)| \geq \epsilon)$.
Thus the proof would require the exhibiting of a particular epsilon with
the property that no matter what delta was employed, there would always exist some x such that x is within a distance delta of a and yet
$f(x)$ and $f(a)$ were not within an epsilon of each other. It goes without
saying that the symbol structure gives a much cleaner expression of the
concept. In particular it clearly indicates the sequence of selection of
the epsilon, delta, and x. The sequence is a major pitfall of many calculus students.

To further illustrate the importance of this concept, we look at
the definitions of a function continuous on a set and a function uniformily continuous on a set. A function is said to be continuous on a set S
if and only if for any point of the set and any arbitrary positive number
epsilon, there is a positive number δ such that all points y of the set
are such that $|x - y| < \delta \Rightarrow |f(x) - f(y)| < \epsilon$. In symbols, we have

with x and y from the domain S and δ and ϵ from the domain of positive numbers:

$$(\forall x)\,(\forall \epsilon)\,(\exists \delta)\,(\forall y)\,(\,|x - y| < \delta \Rightarrow |f(x) - f(y) < \epsilon)\,.$$

A function is said to be *uniformily* continuous on a set S if and only if for any $\epsilon > 0$, there exists a $\delta > 0$ such that for any x and y within a δ of each other we have $f(x)$ and $f(y)$ within an ϵ of each other. In symbols this gives:

$$(\forall \epsilon)\,(\exists \delta)\,(\forall x)\,(\forall y)\,|x - y| < \delta \Rightarrow |f(x) - f(y)| < \epsilon)\,.$$

The only difference between these fundamental definitions is the location of the various quantifiers. As the student undoubtedly realizes now, the symbols express these relationships in a more meaningful manner. This can be further brought out by asking a typical calculus student if it matters whether one is "given the x or the epsilon first in the definition of a continuous function." Since we know that universal quantifiers commute, we see that the difference is immaterial.

The usefulness in the symbols is further expanded in the negations of the two definitions. For continuous functions and uniformily continuous functions, respectively:

$$(\exists x)\,(\exists \epsilon)\,(\forall \delta)\,(\exists y)\,(\,|x - y| < \delta \wedge |f(x) - f(y)| \geqq \epsilon)$$

$$(\exists \epsilon)\,(\forall \delta)\,(\exists x)\,(\exists y)\,(\,|x - y| < \delta \wedge |f(x) - f(y)| \geqq \epsilon)\,.$$

We have introduced three or more quantifiers without any mention of the diagrams of their truth sets. The generalization from two individual variables to more than three follows the idea of multiple product sets. That is, ordered triples, ordered four-tuples, etc. The graphs are progressively more complicated, but the basic devices that we have arrived at should handle most of the elementary logical problems that are usually encountered in mathematics.

EXERCISES (§ 2.)

1. Symbolize the following expressions:

(a) Any triangle is congruent to some triangle and similar to some triangle.

(b) Any triangle is congruent and similar to some triangle.

(c) Two coplanar lines are parallel or they intersect.

2. Simplify the following:

(a) $\forall(x)\ \forall(y)\ (\forall x)\ (\exists y)\ P(x,y)$

(b) $(\forall x)\ \sim(\exists y)\ (\forall z)\ (P(x,y) \Rightarrow\ \sim Q(x,y))$

3. Negate the definitions of convergent and Cauchy sequences given in Exercise 7 in Section §1.

4. An interesting discussion of logic and mathematics is given in W. A. Hijab's article "Logical Quantifiers; An Aid to Clear Thinking" in *American Mathematical Monthly*, Vol. 70 (1963) pp. 77–79. Read and discuss the article.

5. Diagram the truth sets of $|x| < y$ and $x^2 < y^2$ in the set of real numbers crossed with the real numbers. Explain why these diagrams indicate that "If $|x| < y$, then $x^2 < y^2$." is true for all real numbers x and y.

Appendix

THE ORDERED REAL NUMBER FIELD

Equality is the basic relation on the real numbers, and it is assumed to be an equivalence relation. That is, equality satisfies the following postulates:

E 1 (reflexivity) If a is a real number, then $a = a$.

E 2 (symmetry) If two real numbers a and b are such that $a = b$, then $b = a$.

E 3 (transitivity) If three real numbers a, b, and c are such that $a = b$ and $b = c$; then $a = c$.

Addition, $+$, and multiplication, $\cdot$, are the two basic operations on the real numbers. These operations are well-defined* in that they satisfy the following postulates:

$A\,E$ 1 If four real numbers a, b, c, and d are such that $a = b$ and $c = d$; then $a + c = b + d$.

$M\,E$ 2 If four real numbers a, b, c, and d are such that $a = b$ and $c = d$; then $a \cdot c = b \cdot d$.

The real numbers with the operations of addition and multiplication form an algebraic system that is an example of a field. That is, the system satisfies the following postulates:

A 1 (Closure) If a and b are real numbers, then $a + b$ is a real number.

A 2 (Associativity) If a, b, and c are real numbers, then $a + (b + c) = (a + b) + c$.

---

*   In mathematics, "well-defined" does not mean quite what the words suggest. An operation is *well-defined* when equal operands combine to give equal results.

Bibliography

A brief list of texts for additional study.

Ambrose, Alice, and Lazerowitz, Morris, *Fundamentals of Symbolic Logic*, New York: Rinehart and Company, Inc., 1954.

Exner, Robert and Rosskopf, Myron, *Logic in Elementary Mathematics*, New York: McGraw-Hill Book Company, 1959.

Mendelson, Elliott, *Introduction to Mathematical Logic*, Princeton: D. Van Nostrand Company, Inc., 1964.

Quine, Willard Van Orman, *Mathematical Logic*, rev. ed., New York: Harper and Row Publishers, 1962.

Rosser, J. Barkley, *Logic for Mathematicians*, New York: McGraw-Hill Book Company, Inc., 1953.

Suppes, Patrick, *Introduction to Logic*, Princeton: D. Van Nostrand Company, Inc., 1957.

Zehna, Peter W., and Johnson, Robert L., *Elements of Set Theory*, Boston: Allyn and Bacon, Inc., 1962.

Answers to Selected Exercises

Chapter 1

§1, 1. (b) statement
       (c) open sentence
       (d) statement in context
       (e) not a statement
       (h) statement in context
       (i) open sentence
       (j) a statement with unknown truth value
       (k) a false statement
       (n) not a statement. If it is true (false), then it is false (true).

§2, 1. (f) $\sim p$
       (g) $\sim \sim q$ or q
       (i) All men are not outstanding
       (l) $2 \leq 3$

§2, 2. (d) Someone is not here
       (f) All rooms are not pink

§2, 3. (d) Somebody is perfect
       (e) Some integers are not whole numbers
       (f) Hit the ball when it is on the putting green
       (g) Hit mulligans on any tee
       (h) Some lazy students do study

§3·B, 1 (b) $p \lor q$
       (d) $p \lor q$
       (f) $p \lor q$
       (g) $p \land q$
       (k) $p \underline{\lor} q$
       (m) $p \underline{\lor} q$
       (u) All that glitters is not disjunction. In this case, a golden cockerel.

§3·C,1. (c) If the lines are parallel, then they never meet. Parallelism is a sufficient condition for the lines to never meet.

Parallel implies that the lines never meet.
The lines are parallel only if they never meet.

§3·C,3. (a) $\sim r \Rightarrow p$ No rain and no picnic

§3·F,1. (b) $\sim (p \wedge r) \Longleftrightarrow \sim q$
(d) $r \underline{\vee} p$
(e) $(p \vee r) \wedge \sim (p \wedge r)$
(f) $p \downarrow q$

Chapter 2

§2, 1. (a), (b), and (f) are formulas

§2, 2. 14

§2, 3. In the truth table answers, the truth values are stated for the
usual assignment of truth values to the statement variables.
(c) F T
(d) T T T
(e) T T T T T T T T

§2, 4. (e) T T F T F T F T
(f) F F F T F T T T
(i) F F F T F T T F

§3, 1. 3(c) is synthetic;
3(d) is a tautology.

§3, 3. $p \wedge q \equiv (p/q) / (p/q)$
$p \vee q \equiv (p/p) / (q/q)$
$p \underline{\vee} q \equiv ((p/q)/p) / ((q/p)/q)$
$p \Rightarrow q \equiv (p/q)/p$
$p \Longleftrightarrow q \equiv ((p/p) / (q/q)) / (p/q)$
$p \downarrow q \equiv ((p/p) / (q/q)) / ((p/p) / (q/q))$
$\sim p \equiv p/p$

§3, 5. There is not another one.

Chapter 2 (continued)

§3, 6. $\sim$, $/$; $\sim$, $\downarrow$; or $/$, $\downarrow$ but these are not minimal sets.

§3, 8. (a) strong disjunction
        (b) strong disjunction
        (c) weak disjunction

§4, 1. (c) $(p \Rightarrow (q \Rightarrow r)) \Rightarrow ((p \Rightarrow q) \Rightarrow (p \Rightarrow r))$

Chapter 3

§3, 4. (b) conjunction, weak disjunction
        (d) implication
        (e) Sheffer stroke and joint denial

§4, 3. In the row of the tables
        (a) $\vee$: yes, yes
             $\underline{\vee}$: yes, yes
             $\Rightarrow$: no, no
             $/$: no, yes
        (b) $\vee$: yes, yes, no, yes, yes, no, no
             $\underline{\vee}$:   no, no, no, no, no, no, no.
             $\Rightarrow$: yes, yes, no, yes, yes, no, no
             $/$: no, no, no, no, no, no, no

Chapter 4

§1 1.   Invalid, the argument states an improper conclusion; it could not give any of its statements as a proper conclusion.

§1, 3.   Valid

§1, 5.   Valid

§2·A, 6. (a) The proof first gives a contrapositive proof of the if part, then a direct proof of the only if part
     (b) contrapositive

§2·B,1. (b) $((p \wedge q) \Rightarrow r) \wedge ((p \wedge q) \Rightarrow s)$ can be proved instead of $(p \wedge q) \Rightarrow (r \wedge s)$

§2·B,4. (a) $a > 0$, $b > 0$ implies $ab > 0$. $a > 0$ says that $a^{-1} > 0$ and $a^{-1}(ab) > 0$ gives $b > 0$
     (b) $((p \wedge q) \Rightarrow r) \wedge ((p \wedge r) \Rightarrow q)$ is proved instead of the given theorem, $p \Rightarrow (q \Leftrightarrow r)$.

§2·B,9. Assume $a > b$, and $c > 0$ implies $a < b + c$.
  This gives $a - b > 0$. With $a - b$ in the role of c in the implication; we have $a < b + a - b$, i.e., the contradiction $a < a$. The proof is with the *reductio ad absurdum* technique.

§2·B,15. Instead of the given form
$((p \vee q) \wedge (r \vee s)) \Rightarrow (t \vee u)$, prove
$((p \wedge r) \Rightarrow t) \wedge ((p \wedge s) \Rightarrow u) \wedge \cdots \wedge ((q \wedge s) \Rightarrow u)$.

§2·B,18. By trichotomy, $O1$, we know exactly one of $a > 0$ (p), $a = 0$ (q), or $a < 0$ (r); and $b > 0$ (s), $b = 0$ (t), or $b < 0$ (u). The logic of the proof by cases is explained by the complicated tautology
$((p \wedge (q \downarrow r)) \vee (\sim p \wedge (q \vee r)) \wedge (s \wedge \cdots \vee u))$
$(p \wedge s) \Rightarrow w) \wedge ((p \wedge t) \Rightarrow w) \wedge \cdots \wedge ((r \wedge u) \Rightarrow w))$
$\Rightarrow w$ where w is the statement of the theorem.

§2·B,23. (d) The "if" part is proved with a direct proof, then the contrapositive of the "if" part is proved. The proof is incomplete since the "only if" part still needs to be proved.
     (e) The theorem is stated in the form $((p \wedge q) \vee (r \wedge s)) \Rightarrow t$, and a proof is given for $\sim t \Rightarrow (\sim p \wedge \sim s) \vee (\sim r \wedge \sim q))$.

From the tautology
$$((\sim p \wedge \sim s) \vee (\sim r \wedge \sim q)) \Rightarrow \sim((p \wedge q) \vee (r \wedge s)),$$
we see that what amounts to a contrapositive of the
original theorem results.

Chapter 5

§1, 1. (a) $(\forall x)\ Sx$
   (b) $(\exists x)\ Sx$
   (d) $(\exists x)\ Hx$

§1, 2. (a) $G(x)$, an open sentence, domain $---$ things
   (c) not a statement
   (d) p, a statement
   (g) $(\forall x)\ (Cx \Rightarrow Gx)$, statement, domain $---$ animals

§1, 4. (a) $\{1\}$
   (b) $\{-1, 1\}$
   (f) $\{$all real numbers that are not odd multiples of $\pi/2\}$

§2, 1. (a) $(\forall x)\ (Qx \Rightarrow Px)$, A
   (d) $(\exists x)\ (Qx \wedge \sim Px)$, O
   (g) $(\exists x)\ (Px \wedge Qx)$, I

§2, 8. (a) $(\forall x)\ (Mx \Rightarrow Sx)$
   (c) $(\forall x)\ (Dx \Rightarrow (Cx/Tx))$
   (f) $(\forall x)\ (Rx \Rightarrow \sim Ix)$

§3, 1. (b) All functions are not continuous.
   (d) All real numbers are rational if and only if they are
       irrational.
   (g) All neighborhoods of the origin do not contain the point $\propto$.
   (h) There exists a neighborhood of the origin that does not
       contain the point $\propto$.

§3, 6. (a) valid
   (c) valid
   (d) invalid

§3, 9. (b) To know that everything is P or Q, does not imply that
       everything is P or that everything is Q.

§ 4,   2.   (a) $(\forall x) (Qx \Rightarrow p) \iff (\forall x) (\sim p \Rightarrow \sim Qx)$
$\iff (\sim p \Rightarrow (\forall x) \sim Qx)$
$\iff (\sim p \Rightarrow \sim (\exists x) Qx)$
$\iff ((\exists x) Qx \Rightarrow p)$

(d) $(\exists x) (Qx \wedge p) \iff (\exists x) \sim (Qx \Rightarrow \sim p)$
$\iff \sim (\forall x) (Qx \Rightarrow \sim p)$
$\iff \sim ((\exists x) Qx \Rightarrow \sim p)$
$\iff (p \wedge (\exists x) Qx)$

§ 4,   3.   (b) valid
(d) invalid
(e) invalid

§ 4,   4.   (a) T
(b) T $= \tau ((\forall x)(Px \wedge \sim Qx) \vee \sim (\forall x)(Px \wedge \sim Qx))$
$= \tau (((\forall x)(Px \wedge \sim Qx) \vee (\exists x)(\sim Px \vee Qx))$
(d) T

Chapter 6

§ 1,   3.   In the domain of integers:
"Every integer precedes some integer" is true, i.e.,
$(\forall x)(\exists y)$.
"Some integer is preceded by every integer" is false, i.e.,
$(\exists y)(\forall x)$.

§ 1,   5.   (a) T
(c) T
(d) F
(h) F
(i) F
(j) T

Index

A

Absolute values, 73
Absurdity, law of, 36
Addition, 120
  law of, 36
Affirmative, particular, 91
  universal, 90
Affirmo, 91
Algebra of the real numbers, 44, 49
Algebra of statements, 44-51
Alternate punctuation systems, 41
Alternate logic techniques, 57
Ambiguity of or, 13
Ampersand, 12n
Analysis, diagram method, 106
"And," 12
Antecedent, 16
  conjunction of, 69
Argument, 52-56
  analysis of, 95
  and existential statement, 104
Argument form, 52, 53
  classifying, 54
Aristotle, 101
Assertion, negation of, 9
Associative law, 44-45
Associative operators, 44
Associativity, 120, 121
Assumption, contradictory, 55

B

Biconditional, 19-22, 41
  in conclusion, 67
  sequences of, 105
Binary base, 3n
Binary base numerical system, 3n
Binary operators, 10-24
  associative, 44
Blended matrix method, 29

Bound formulas, 87
Braces, 25
Brackets, 25

C

Cairns, Stewart S., 77n
Capital letters, as punctuation, 42
Carroll, Lewis, 103
Case investigation, 72
Cauchy sequence, 116, 119
Change in logical form, 57
Closure, 120, 121
Comma, 25n
Commutative laws, 44, 45-46
Commutativity, 121
Complex statement, symbolizing, 117
Conclusion, 16, 52
  biconditional in, 67
  conjunction in, 65-66
  implication in, 69
  improper, 53
  operators in, 64
Condition, 16, 52
Conjoined statements, 11
Conjunction, 12, 41
  of antecedent, 69
  in conclusion, 65-66
  and disjunction, 84
  in hypothesis, 65-66
  and implication, 47
  and inclusive disjunction, 47
  negation of, 14
  punctuating, 42
Conjunction changes, 64
Conjunction techniques, 67
Connectives, 13
  symbols for, 12
Consequence, 16
  negation of, 69
Consistency, 53